MW00612956

Love,
Marie C

ISBN: 0-9723939-0-0

Cover Design — Through These Gates
by Joe Leone

Editing
by Johannah Adams

Photo
by Kenneth Parker

Manufactured in the United States of America

Dedicated to the memory of Mildred Nelson and the wonderful doctors and staff at the Bio-Medical Center who follow in her footsteps.

With special thanks to Liz Jonas, who continues the commitment of bringing healing and hope to people the world over, and to my daughter, Marta Christine Nawn, who never failed to support me.

Disclaimer

This book is not intended to be a medical guide. I do not have a medical background, and it is not my intent to give advice. It is written to inform the reader of the alternative approach I took. It is a personal history as I lived it. I am not in any way promoting alternative cancer treatments as options that will work for everyone.

Foreword

This book is written to tell you of my experiences, and about a place where there are caring, dedicated and knowledgeable doctors and staff outside the realm of the basic treatment of cancer as most people know or think of it. I also hope to inspire or motivate you to take the time to consider the type of "treatment" or "therapy" best for you.

There is far more to this unique place I call "the Clinic" than one book can tell, but if this is the first time you have heard of the Bio-Medical Center, it is a beginning.

When one is diagnosed with cancer, in all likelihood it has probably been in the body for a considerable length of time. To take a few days to consider any and all possibilities only makes good sense.

From NATIVE AMERICAN WISDOM

...everything on earth has a purpose,
every disease an herb to cure it,
and every person a mission.

Mourning Dove (Christine Quintasket)
(1888-1936)
Salish

Introduction

In writing this book, I am not trying to convince you that the procedures and treatments set up by the American Medical Association (AMA) should not be followed, but to remind you that you have a choice, and to bring the alternative method I followed to light. This is your life, your body, and should you wish to follow the road less traveled, it is available for those who wish to take it.

Your doctor may recommend or suggest a procedure to follow, but he or she cannot and should not tell you what to do. All possible alternatives should be thoroughly explained so that you can make the decision you feel is right for you. If you feel you have not received adequate answers and explanations, or have not been given options, it is your right to go elsewhere. Always remember—the final word is yours. So, before you sign all the papers giving permission to follow a particular course of treatment (and excuse unforeseen consequences), think it over carefully. Interestingly, it is not necessary to sign any release papers at the Bio-Medical Center, and never in their long, long history have they been sued.

Long ago, I decided that quality of life is fundamentally important. To extend life only to suffer is not living. When I expressed these thoughts to my surgeon after my surgery, he could only answer with "I hear you talking." However, as he explained to me, he was a man of science, so he could not think of "herbal" treatment as a cure. Ultimately, as time went on and he could see how I was progressing, he became interested in this concept (which was new to him) and said, "we'll do this your way."

Herbs of one kind or another are the basis for most prescription drugs. But for some reason if these same herbs are taken in a non-prescription form it is usually frowned upon, and in some cases even referred to as quackery. This is difficult to understand. It is also hard to comprehend why the medical profession in America seem to approve using drugs and performing procedures on patients which all too often make them feel sicker. But when confronted with a way to combat cancer which promotes health (as I have observed from people I've met) and has no side effects, it is frowned upon.

There are many experiences to relate and heartwarming stories to tell, but without a doubt the only way to truly appreciate a place like the Bio-Medical Center is to see it firsthand yourself, and talk to the patients, doctors, and staff you encounter.

It would have been easier to simply keep quiet about my trips to Mexico and everything that transpired, but almost from the very beginning I believed there was a reason this happened to me, and the fact that it should all be recorded was on my mind almost from the onset.

For many months I kept my experiences from friends and co-workers, but eventually it seemed the time had come to relate all the events that took place, and I began going through all the notes I had taken since I was first diagnosed. Everything happened just as it is told in this book; only the names, in some cases, have been changed to protect identities.

The idea to actually put my experiences in book form seemed to clearly emerge (from what I consider the cobwebs of my mind) after a conversation with a friend of mine. The conversation took place after I had been on the Hoxsey Therapy for some months, and had never felt better. The subject of cancer treatments came up, and she was relating the experiences of people she knew who were, at the time, going through radiation or chemotherapy. During the course of the discussion she made the statement: "Everyone does his own thing. Everyone decides what is best." Not wishing to be argumentative, or ready to relate my own experiences, I agreed with her.

At home that evening I thought about her statement and my silence on the subject, and I was furious with myself. How could she possibly say people decide anything themselves when it comes to cancer treatments? Her statement was assuredly incorrect. When a person is told they have cancer, it is like a red flag going up, and they rely totally on their doctor's recommendation. They blindly follow the procedures and practices he sets up, and (except, possibly, in extremely rare cases) there are no decisions of any kind made by the patient. And it seems the thought of questioning or asking about alternatives never seems to cross their mind.

How many would choose another course if they were aware there is another way? Every time I hear of a death, or someone's long and painful suffering, I wonder how many would choose the harsh treatments prescribed by the medical establishment of this country if they realized they had a choice—that there is another way. And, if they heard about an alternative method, would they have the courage to defy their doctor and try this unorthodox approach? I don't know—surely they all would not—but I'm sure some would. For them this book is written.

Table of Contents

Part 1

The First Two Years

Chapter 1

The Phone Call

It started out as such an ordinary day.

In my wildest dreams I could not have imagined that it would be the beginning of an incredible journey for me. As usual, I was trying to postpone leaving the comfort of my bed for as long as possible. My cat Christmas, sensing my reluctance to stir, was nudging my face with her cold nose, reminding me it was breakfast time. It was a Thursday morning, bright and warm, and all seemed well with the world.

After feeding Christmas and having breakfast myself, I found myself running late. As I hurried to finish dressing, I knew my day would start once again with a friendly barrage of harassment from my co-workers. I work as secretary to the Chief of Police in the Town of Holden, and the officers invariably tease me and make the most of the few minutes I might stroll in late. Thinking of it made me smile as I drove the short distance from my house to the police station.

As expected, I entered the building and was greeted with a short "is it noon already?" followed by a friendly smile. I smiled in return, and then entered the Chief's office. The Chief is a tall, lean man, given to frequent workouts and expecting the same interest in physical fitness of his officers. He was sitting behind his large wooden desk, having already finished going through all the reports from the previous night. After a little small talk, I gathered up the reports and brought them to my desk in the adjoining room. I was soon wrapped up in sorting, filing, and other tasks, interrupted occasionally by officers coming in—Thursday is payday and one can expect to see most everyone on that day.

It is not unusual for me to receive phone calls requesting reports or information of one type or another, so I gave little thought to a phone call when I was told it was for me. However, this call was personal. On the other end of the line was my doctor, telling me she had checked my recent mammogram and that something looked "suspicious." My immediate reaction was that she was overreacting. After all, there is absolutely no history of cancer in my family. It was, in fact, only by chance that I'd had the mammogram at all. While changing insurance companies recently, I was required to find a new primary care physician, who insisted that the mammogram be done. It was apparent that the doctor was surprised by my reluctance to accept what she was saying, but she quickly went on to inform me that she had already made arrangements for me to meet with a surgeon. "You owe it to yourself," she added. I was then turned over to another party and the date for my appointment was confirmed.

After the phone call it was hard to keep my mind on my work. My thoughts wandered back to the day I had the mammogram. A second x-ray of my right breast had been taken; the nurse explained that something was not "clear." This would undoubtedly turn out to be the "suspicious" something the doctor was referring to. Unlike many of my friends who sat on pins and needles after a mammogram until they received the "all-clear" call from their doctor, my mammogram had been all but forgotten. Now, ironically, I was in the position they feared.

The appointment with the surgeon was arranged for a few days later. Dr. West, a pleasant man, used the word "suspicious" again, and explained the tumor was very small and should be removed to make certain it was not cancerous. It seems that had it been slightly larger, a biopsy would be done first, but because it was so small would be completely removed. The surgery would take place on a Thursday, a couple of weeks after the initial phone call.

Leaving his office after this short consultation with the surgery date set left me with a strange, unsettled feeling. The doctor had been very matter-of-fact about the whole thing, but then why shouldn't he be? — he had probably said the same thing to a hundred other patients. It was the look on the face of his nurse, though, that haunted me. As she ushered me into the doctor's office I noticed a look of compassion on her face, and I sensed she was feeling sorry for me. Did she know something I was not told, something I should know? I told myself it was my imagination, it was too soon for anyone to feel sorry, this was just something "suspicious" and would probably turn out to be nothing.

However, with the surgery date looming ahead of me, thoughts about the possibility of cancer never left me. As anyone who has gone through this experience will tell you, a thousand different things come to mind. For me, the thought that kept coming back was about a conversation I had with my friend Bonny some years before. Bonny had a neighbor whose mother, Eva, had been diagnosed with cancer. Eva's doctor had told her that unless she had her leg amputated she would probably only live six months. Eva consulted two other doctors at the time, each telling her amputation was the only thing that would save her life. When Eva told her daughter that she was not having her leg amputated—period—her daughter found out about a place in Mexico, which successfully treated cancer with herbs. She asked her mother if she would consider going there, and Eva agreed to go and try it. At the time of my conversation with Bonny, a considerable length of time had passed since Eva's visit to Mexico, and she was still alive, well, and had both legs. I remember saying that I would certainly go to this place if I were ever diagnosed with cancer. Of course, when one does not expect the unexpected, this is an easy statement to make. I didn't know where the place was or anything about it. Did I really mean what I said? It seemed to fall into a category with statements one might absentmindedly make about how much fun it would be to hang glide or shoot the rapids on some wild river—occasions which would most likely never arise, and so one would never actually have to contend with them.

However, somehow my thoughts seemed to forever return to that conversation with Bonny. Was Eva still well after all this time? I had an inexplicable urge to find out, to talk to her if possible, and to find out more about the place in Mexico. I decided to call Bonny, relay all of this to her, and ask about Eva. Bonny was very understanding and was able to put me in contact with Eva, who in return gave me a brief rundown of her experiences and the telephone number to the Clinic. She told me it is called the Bio-Medical Center and that the cancer treatment they use is known as "Hoxsey." The most unbelievable thing I found out, however, was the fact that it had been approximately twenty years since she visited the Clinic.

The next day I called the Clinic. Once I had the telephone number it seemed right for me to do this, and to get whatever information I could. I talked to one of the doctors and he said that if I thought I had cancer I should not have surgery yet, and briefly explained why not. Hearing this was more upsetting than anything imaginable. My desire to go to the Clinic right then and there was overwhelming. I dreaded the thought of surgery, but I knew that everyone in my family would probably be against my going to Mexico to begin with, and to go without knowing if I actually had cancer was out of the question. I had no alternative other than to go through with the surgery as scheduled. Cancer had to be confirmed before I could make such a trip.

I decided at this time to bring the subject up to my daughter, Marta.

Later, in thinking about the phone conversation with Marta, I realized it must have all been rather bizarre for her. It isn't every day your mother calls to say she is scheduled for surgery and that cancer is a possibility. No wonder her reaction was one of rejection, insisting that it would turn out to be nothing, that everything would be OK, etc. It was not possible, as far as she was concerned, that I could have cancer. When I went on to say that I was planning to go to Mexico if the tumor was malignant, I'm sure she thought I was a little mad. Where did I come up with such an idea? She simply could not imagine that I was serious. Mexico, of all places! However, since she was convinced that the tumor would be benign, and such a trip would never take place, she agreed to accompany me if necessary.

Chapter 2

You Owe it to Yourself

The pre-surgery exam a couple of days prior to the actual surgery turned out to be extremely traumatic for me. Perhaps the thought of what was to come really hit me then. All I can remember is that all the reassurances about what a fine doctor I had did nothing to comfort or console me.

The following Thursday morning I was at the hospital preparing for this "minor" operation. I could hardly wait until it was over. It was explained that I would only be given enough anesthesia to deaden the pain, but it was added that virtually all patients fall asleep. Believe me, I am no martyr, but I was determined not to end up asleep. Somehow I felt that I would be in control only if I stayed awake. Perhaps it was my reluctance to have the operation in the first place that made me feel this way, or perhaps it was all the horror stories I had heard about women waking up after such operations and finding out that the surgery performed was more horrendous than they'd anticipated. Whatever the reason, while I did manage to stay awake, I was certainly not in control.

After surgery I was advised that, as predicted, the tumor was very small. The entire tumor and a small amount of tissue surrounding it had been removed. The incision was about two inches long, but in spite of the small size it was very painful. I was sent home that afternoon, sore and swollen. I was given a prescription for pain pills and was told to put ice packs on for about a week. My plan was to return to work the following Monday, which I felt would not be a problem since the nursing staff expressed no great concern about "so small an operation." Also, I had three days—Friday and the weekend—which I felt would be more than adequate to recover.

After three uncomfortable and for the most part sleepless days and nights, I returned to work. The pain pills were of little comfort, as they tended to upset my stomach; the ice packs, however, seemed to help. I had decided not to tell anyone at the station about the possibility of cancer, and most of the officers (I believe) did not even realize that I'd had surgery of any kind, since I was only out of work for two days. It was a difficult week for me; it was hard to believe such a "small" operation could be so painful. As soon as I returned home each evening I attempted to get comfort from the ice pack. How horrible it must be for those whose surgeries are much greater than mine, I thought.

The following Friday I had an appointment to see the surgeon, Dr. West, but I felt I would hear from the lab long before that. I was wrong. The entire week passed without my hearing a word about the cancer biopsy.

Since I had contacted the Bio-Medical Center they had sent me a brochure which I decided, towards the end of the week, to show my daughter. Marta looked it over but had little to say, obviously thinking that my interest in the herbal treatment offered in Mexico was more than premature. By this time, however, I did not think the trip was all that impossible.

When Friday finally arrived I felt that I knew what I was going to be told. Perhaps I really knew from the beginning and that was my reason for contacting Eva, or perhaps working at a police station had made me more aware of the policy of quickly notifying family members when a relative was involved in an accident, to assure them injuries were minimal or non-existent. In cases of severe injury or death, the call would be withheld until a supervisor could relay the information. In my case, no call was made. Dr. West would be the one to give me the results at the Friday appointment. In addition, I was asked to bring someone with me for the visit. Perhaps bringing someone along is standard procedure, but I knew that I wanted to make this trip alone.

My appointment was late in the day. Dr. West's nurse was more than a little upset that I had come by myself. I told her I was quite all right, but she again repeated that I should not have come alone, and then apologized, saying it would be a little while before the doctor could see me, because it had been a very busy day. It was now very clear that no one but the doctor himself was going to talk to me.

Dr. West is a man approximately fifty years old, cordial but to the point. He said that the tumor was found to be cancerous and he advised more surgery right away, because the tissue around the area should be removed. Here I was, hearing the worst news possible, yet I found myself saying that before I would consider any further surgery I was going to get another opinion. Needless to say he found my attitude completely negative, unlike other patients who no doubt immediately agreed to whatever was suggested. He then said that on the following Wednesday several doctors would be at the hospital, all qualified to tell me about the options available. He said, "You owe it to yourself to talk to these doctors and hear what they have to say." The fact that these doctors knew best was made very clear to me. I assured him that I would return on Wednesday, thinking to myself that the little saying "you owe it to yourself" must be a very frequently used phrase.

As I left the hospital after this consultation, thinking about what I had just heard, I was surprisingly calm. I can still remember the day clearly. It was late and the sun was low in the sky, casting a kind of orange glow on everything. The air was clear from an afternoon rain and the sidewalk was still wet. As I walked towards the parking lot a comforting feeling flooded over me. I felt grateful and peaceful. I knew where I was going and I knew what I was going to do, and somehow I felt that everything was going to be all right.

Somehow, my inexplicable urge to find out about the Bio-Medical Center now made sense. I wondered if it was possible that I had been guided. Somehow I felt this was the case. Somehow I felt this was something I was meant to do. Would my family agree? In my mind I went over the approaching conversations and what I would say: I was going to Mexico and I was not going to have more surgery at this time as advised. I would return to the hospital on Wednesday to hear what the other doctors had to say, and perhaps reconsider the additional surgery, but only after hearing the suggestions made at the Clinic. I would make reservations for myself and my daughter to fly to San Diego (the Clinic is located just over the border) and this would be done as quickly as possible.

As expected, when I broke the news to my husband he was horrified. He thought I was out of my mind not making immediate plans for more surgery. My plan to go to Mexico seemed even more ridiculous to him. My son echoed my husband's feelings. I tried to explain—and hoped they would understand—this was my body and my decision, and this was what I intended to do. My husband would not let the subject drop, and kept insisting I was making the biggest mistake ever. However, nothing he could say was going to make me change my mind. Clearly my stubborn Norwegian nature had come out.

The next day I called Marta to give her the news and tell her that we were going to Mexico. I would make the reservations for the two of us to fly to San Diego as soon as possible. I had checked with the Clinic to make certain there were no upcoming Mexican holidays I might not be aware of (not knowing if the Clinic would close on such days) and was assured there were none in the immediate future. The Clinic gave me the name of a motel in San Diego which gave discounts to Clinic patients, and also about a lady named Leona Rogers who transports people to the Clinic every day. I only had to call her on the evening of our arrival and she would pick us up the following morning in time to get us to the Clinic by 8:30. No passport would be necessary to go across the border, and no advance reservations were needed at the Clinic. Leona would be available again at the end of the day to return us to our lodging. I found out that, in most cases, one's first visit generally consists of spending only one day at the Clinic. Only in more extreme cases is a person asked to come back a second or third day.

By giving all the information to Marta, I hoped to make her feel as comfortable as possible before embarking on a trip which I knew seemed strange and alien to her—not to mention a trip she'd been sure she would never take. I also knew that California had never been high on the list of places she desired to visit, and she hated the thought of flying. Besides this she had two small boys at home, and her primary concern would of course be for their well-being during her absence. However the trip would be short, only four days, with one (possibly two) spent at the Clinic. In spite of all the questions she undoubtedly had, and the arrangements she would have to make before she could leave, she expressed little of them to me. Most importantly, Marta did not make any negative remarks such as those I'd heard the night before. Hopefully her husband would take control on the home front, making the trip a little easier for her.

The reservations were made. The trip would be in exactly two weeks.

Chapter 3

Recommendations

As I anxiously began to think about the trip, I also contemplated the appointment scheduled for the following Wednesday, when several different avenues might be suggested by several different doctors. The impression I had was that the visit would be fairly informal but at the same time informative. I would compare the recommendations I received that day with the Clinic's advice.

On Wednesday I returned to the hospital and Dr. West's office. The visit was not at all what I expected; I was totally unprepared. I was ushered into an examining room, where each doctor came to see me individually, examined my still sore and swollen surgery, looked at my history, and made his or her recommendation. After each doctor finished and I sat waiting for the next one, I made notes of what I had been told. This is a partial sampling:

Dr. Ellis recommended additional surgery, which involved removing more tissue and all of the lymph nodes on my right side. Because I was reluctant to do this, he informed me that if I did not follow this route I would be placed on a five-year program emphasizing radiation, which could cause nausea, hot flashes and discharge. He did not think chemotherapy would be necessary. He strongly recommended surgery, while obviously (it seemed to me) making sure the alternative looked as unattractive as possible.

Dr. Jones recommended "modified surgery," which to him was the removal of the entire breast and all of the lymph nodes. Only a doctor or some totally uninterested third party could possibly think of this as "modified" as far as I was concerned. If I should opt not to have the entire breast removed, a choice which seemed ridiculous to him since plastic surgery was available, then his second option was to remove all of the lymph nodes. If these showed no cancer, then radiation of the breast and underarm would be necessary. He explained the side effects of radiation as hardening of the breast, changes in the texture of the skin, loss of energy, etc. He also gave me the additional information that it actually did not matter what procedure was followed—modified or radical (where not only the breast is removed but all tissue right down to the bones of the chest) or a lumpectomy— statistically, 25% of the patients do not make it.

One of the doctors made a point of telling me how much his patients all loved him. Why he felt it necessary to provide me with this bit of information I cannot guess, but at the time I decided it was not essential to know the reason and I did not choose to pursue it.

There was not one doctor who did not think that more surgery was an absolute must. One doctor, in fact, spoke of a girl who recently had both breasts removed as a precaution because there was cancer in her family. He simply could not understand my reluctance, since it all seemed so simple to him.

As part of the questioning, all of the doctors asked me what medication, if any, I had been taking before my cancer was diagnosed. I told all of them I had been taking an estrogen-enhancing drug for a considerable length of time (which I recall they all made note of), but just one—the only woman—suggested that I no longer take it.

The last doctor I was scheduled to talk to was the plastic surgeon. I adamantly refused to see him, explaining to the nurse that I was going elsewhere for another opinion before considering any kind of treatment or further surgery. Therefore, plastic surgery or any procedures associated with it was definitely not in my plans at this time. Maybe later. Maybe…

Apparently, my decision not to meet with the plastic surgeon was not at all comprehended by his nurse; she assumed my refusal was an oversight of some kind. She called me the next day to set up this "missed" appointment, and when I told her I was not interested, I got the feeling I had quite possibly made a lifetime enemy. She simply could not imagine that I had intentionally decided against seeing him.

As it turned out, the meetings took all morning, and then in the afternoon the five doctors I had seen conferred to compare their recommendations and decide what I should do. They returned in a group, with the following recommendation which I'm sure they thought would be agreeable to me (apparently not having too many patients question their expertise): They decided that breast surgery, i.e., removal of the entire breast, was not necessary because they felt that I was 100% cancer free at this time. I thought this collective response remarkable after listening to them individually. However, they stated that they could be wrong "since no one can ever be sure," and they wanted to remove at least one lymph node and a little more tissue around the tumor area—then they wanted to schedule me for the radiation treatment.

I replied that I would not have surgery at this time, nor would I have one lymph node removed, because I had previously been told that although it was possible that only one lymph node might be cancerous, how would anyone possibly know which one that might be? Also, I informed them that I would not start radiation at this time because I was going elsewhere for another opinion. They wanted to know where, so I said it was a place outside of San Diego— feeling that if I said "Mexico" the idea would be met with even more contempt than I already sensed. They said that to go to California was senseless, that I would be told the same thing there, and my insurance would probably not cover it. They wanted to know the name of the hospital, name of the doctor and various other details. I told them I could not yet provide all of this information, but it was my intention to go and to find out for myself what might be said, and that the matter of payment was my concern, not theirs.

One doctor then said my problem was that I had been "too well" all my life, so I was just having a hard time accepting the facts. It was becoming increasingly clear that most patients blindly follow whatever suggestions and recommendations a doctor makes, and more than likely the most drastic option was usually advised.

After listening to the doctors and being questioned so intensely, I finally said "I usually like a glass of sherry after supper, but tonight I will definitely have two." One doctor found humor in the statement, the rest did not.

That day was, without a doubt, the worst of my life. No wonder women who experience it are left devastated and confused. The memory and knowledge of friends or relatives who have succumbed to this dreaded disease only make it more terrifying, so the majority of women are propelled into whatever is recommended by their doctors, and this is done immediately.

In spite of my thankfulness that there was another way, another avenue to explore before making up my mind about what to do, the day's horror (that is the only word I can think of to explain it) left me feeling numb and exhausted. Once at home I attempted to explain the events of the day to my husband, showing him the notes I had taken, and telling him I was glad there was another place to go. He immediately, once again, voiced the opinion that I was making the biggest mistake of my life by not listening to these knowledgeable doctors who treat cancer every day and obviously know what they are doing. "Isn't America in the forefront of medicine?" I remember him saying. "Surely," he pressed on, "what is done here is better by far than any other place you could go." The Bio-Medical Center was in the quackery department as far as he was concerned. Coupled with this, well-meaning relatives had entered the picture, and all were in agreement with what he was saying.

It seemed I was definitely correct. Two glasses of sherry would be in order for the night.

Chapter 4

Another World, Another Place

The day finally came. It was Wednesday, September 6th, just a couple of weeks after my surgery, and we were on our way. As we boarded the plane, the only thing I knew for sure was that Leona Rogers would meet us the following morning and transport us over the border to the Clinic. It was comforting to have my daughter with me, but I felt that her thoughts were quite different than mine. She undoubtedly felt that all her negative thoughts about California would soon be confirmed, and I couldn't even imagine what she might be thinking about the Clinic in Tijuana, but she did not say anything. I thought of all the opposition I had so stubbornly managed to overcome, and now that I had come this far the realization of how unfamiliar this experience was, closed in on me. There were so many unanswered questions. Was I jumping into what might be the biggest mistake of my life? I tried to put all negative thoughts from my mind, remembering the warm, reassuring feeling I had when I left Dr. West's office knowing I would make this trip. And, I thought, except for Eva who had made this trip before me I knew of no one else who survived cancer for over twenty years.

When we left Massachusetts it was a typical summer day, dewy and very green as it always is before the fall foliage season. The trees were still at their darkest, without a hint of the brilliant colors that New England is so well known for. In the central part of the State where I live, the many wooded areas were still providing cooling shade to the many deer and other wild animals. Once we reached our destination however, the scene was completely different. We stepped into a tropical land of palm trees and flowers, making it difficult not to think of our journey as a vacation—purely a pleasure trip.

We waited only a short time before the shuttle from our hotel arrived and the driver, a friendly, tanned, dark-haired San Diegan named Mark, made us feel entirely welcome. We commented on the numerous varieties of palm trees, which Mark said was frequently one of the first things people noticed when visiting San Diego for the first time. As we drove along he gave us a brief "travel log" of places to see and things to do, obviously knowing the city like the back of his hand. No doubt this would be a great vacation spot, and I even sensed Marta's approval.

The motel that had been recommended was actually a couple of separate two-story buildings. It was conveniently located, clean and comfortable. After settling in and making the phone call to Leona Rogers to let her know that we would be going to the Clinic in the morning, we decided to do a little exploring. There were a few shops and restaurants close by, and while strolling along the unfamiliar street the newness of what was to come was suddenly overwhelming. Perhaps reality was setting in, or perhaps it was no more than a long day of travel, but I suddenly felt exhausted. I had been told not to eat anything after 8:00 PM, and this would surely not be a problem since that would be 11:00 PM Massachusetts' time.

We selected a restaurant and while lingering over coffee it became evident that the pleasant surroundings had a positive effect on Marta. She suggested that it would be fun to do a little sightseeing before it was time to go home, time permitting. We decided to follow one or two of Mark's suggestions if possible. Not until the following day, however, would we know what our schedule would be. Would we be expected to return again on Friday? Would it be possible that we might even be asked to return a third day? What would it be like? Would it be like anything I was familiar with or would it be entirely strange to me? It was a time when my imagination ran wild.

Fortunately after retiring early I slept well, and the following morning we went down to the motel lobby to await Leona. At precisely 8:00 AM, as Marta was helping herself to complimentary coffee and a muffin (I was not to eat breakfast), two tan station wagons pulled up to the lobby door. On each, in large brown letters, was written "T.L.C. - TENDER LOVING CARE." I sensed Marta's reaction, and almost heard her thinking, "Is this for real?" or "You must be kidding." I was reminded of businesses which used adjectives such as "Perfect," "Exceptional," "Guaranteed," "Integrity" or the like, which all too often failed to live up to these wonderfully descriptive words. Would this once again be the case? Certainly we would find out soon enough.

Leona, a warm, grandmotherly woman, was the driver of the first car, and Dennis, a rather tall, thin, blond man, possibly in his forties, was the driver of the second. Marta and I got into Leona's car, and other people who had also been waiting got into the station wagon driven by Dennis. Leona explained that she had been driving patients over the border for years and said that Dennis had been doing the same for a considerable length of time.

Besides Leona, Marta, and myself, there were four other women in the car. There was a middle-aged woman from Wisconsin returning for a checkup, a young-looking woman from northern California accompanied by her daughter, and a lady who said she was returning for her seventeenth visit. The woman from northern California said this was her second visit. She explained that her doctor in the states had removed a tumor from her neck some months before and when he wanted to do more surgery, which would remove her voice box, she opted for a visit to the Clinic. Her first visit had been in June (three months before) and she felt she was doing well.

As soon as we left the city, the scene changed dramatically. Gone were the colorful flowers and blossoming shrubs. We traveled along on a broad highway, bordered by miscellaneous businesses of one type or another. There were palm trees along the highway, and low mountains could be seen in the distance. For the most part everything looked brown and dry, but I thought perhaps it was the time of the year, remembering a trip to Texas in the heat of the summer when it was terribly hot and nothing was green. However, the broad, flat highway we were on was well traveled. Traffic was heavy in both directions. The twenty-minute ride went quickly, the traffic increasing as we arrived at the Mexican border.

It was just a short distance to the border, which we crossed by driving through a gateway, but it could have been miles the transformation was so dramatic. As we drove past uninterested border guards we passed into another world. Suddenly there were people everywhere. Numerous vendors walked back and forth, displaying on their persons every conceivable kind of merchandise, in every imaginable color. There were old men, old women, children and even mothers with babies, which they managed to carry along with whatever they had to sell. The scene was at once noisy and gaudy, a stark contrast to the quiet, colorless ride from San Diego.

Our car passed quickly through this bustling area and followed a road that climbed upwards into a residential area. Here it was peaceful, the street lined with homes built primarily of stucco or brick, many with tile roofs and trim, surrounded by high decorative metal fences. As we neared the top of the hill the Clinic, which looked like a large attractive house, came into view. The Clinic also had front gates, but these were wide open and we drove in and around a circular driveway up to a large front door. In the center of the driveway was a large round birdcage partially covered with vines, containing a variety of colorful birds. Stepping from the car with birdsong filling the air was almost like entering an aviary. Dennis explained that the birds were Mildred Nelson's hobby. (Maybe a clever ploy to keep one's mind on other things? — the possibility did pop into my mind.) It was such an unexpected but pleasant surprise, almost as if the birds were welcoming everyone. Before I even entered the building it was clear this was not going to be like any other hospital or clinic I had ever been in.

Over-hanging the front entrance was a large two-story high archway. The front door itself was of heavy wood, and truly lovely. The setting, one had to admit, was pleasant. It was not hard to feel at ease. I wondered how Marta felt, but no matter what she thought at the moment I knew she was here to find out as much as she could about the place, and I knew she would not be timid in the endeavor. As for myself, I could only hope that if there were other surprises they would be no more unpleasant than finding birds on the premises.

We entered a large foyer and found that other people had arrived ahead of us. The most prominent feature of the foyer, on the wall directly in front of us, was a large six-panel mural of a silver dove and a rainbow, brightly painted red, yellow, green, blue and purple. With the exception of the rainbow everything was painted the palest, softest blue, which was accentuated by the beautiful dark woodwork throughout. The only other decorations were the large green plants placed here and there. From the foyer a large waiting room could be seen, and hallways lead both left and right from the front door.

Two large desks, one flanking either side of the doorway, were equipped with state-of-the-art computers. The desk on the right was for new patients and the one on the left was designated for returning patients. Marta and I headed for the desk on the right, but it was evident that most of the people there that morning were returning patients; the desk on the left was much the busier of the two. The women behind the desks were both attractive and friendly, and as I filled out my paperwork (which asked for my medical background but, significantly, lacked a "no responsibility" release form), I couldn't help but notice that one of the receptionists was sipping coffee from a Bugs Bunny mug.

Dennis, who seemed to be assisting in whatever way he could and was obviously knowledgeable about all aspects of the Clinic, stopped to talk to us for a few minutes while I finished my paperwork. Marta and I had been admiring the building, and Dennis explained that a member of the Mexican underworld had built it, but just as the building was nearing completion the man found himself in trouble with the authorities, possibly tax evasion, and the house ended up under the gavel. It was the general consensus and opinion that the building was not intended to be his home, but rather that it was to be used as a brothel. When it was put up for auction Mildred Nelson was able to procure it for the Clinic, fulfilling her determination to provide a pleasant place for patients.

After our short discussion with Dennis we went down the hall on the right where four small changing rooms were located within a larger room, the doors carefully numbered 1, 2, 3 and 4. On one wall hung two Frederick Remington prints, and in the center of the room was a large desk containing the assorted items necessary for blood tests. Large windows overlooked part of the garden, and a door leading outside was wide open. There were a few chairs along one wall, some already occupied by patients who were obviously ready for their tests.

Like me, all new patients as well as those returning had been given a number that would be used instead of names on all tests, etc., to be done that day. My number was "91." I was told that the first thing on the agenda would be a urinalysis, but first I was given a green robe that I was to wear for the better part of the day.

Now, it is not that I have any objection to wearing a long green wrap-around robe, but I could not help feeling that this requirement definitely had a humorous side. As I walked out of the changing room dressed in my new attire, it seemed like I had just joined some kind of secret green-robe fraternity. In the waiting area were several patients, males and females of various shapes and sizes, all looking essentially the same—except for their shoes. There was a green robe with sandals, a green robe with cowboy boots, a green robe with black dress shoes (that looked like they belonged at a board meeting), and green robes with all varieties of tennis and running shoes. If I looked in the least bit peculiar, I was certainly not alone!

More people arrived, green-robed individuals accompanied by friends or relatives. Most of the people seemed to quickly become engaged in various discussions relating to the different medical experiences they'd had, both in the States and at the Clinic. Returning patients, familiar with the way the Clinic is run, were obviously comfortable with the process as well as each other. Marta was taking full advantage of this opportunity to engage in conversation with as many people as possible, and because everyone was so friendly, this was an easy thing to do.

How unlike the atmosphere in a hospital or waiting room in the States, I thought, where it would be extremely rare for someone to openly express their feelings, concerns, and medical history with the stranger sitting next to them.

While thinking about this it was suddenly my turn for the blood test, a procedure I was not looking forward to. Two people were taking blood this morning, one a female nurse and the other a man, possibly also a nurse, although he was wearing a very casual plaid shirt (which didn't seem of the least to concern anyone). I was assigned to the man, a fact that left me extremely grateful since he was almost painless in performing this unpleasant necessity. He asked me about allergies, and since I was not aware of any, my arm was rubbed as a precaution to test for any possibilities along that line.

The next step for me would be x-rays, which were done in an adjacent building. Marta and I left through the open door and entered the garden, where the presence of the birds was immediately evident. The short walk was far more pleasant than walking down a conventional hospital hallway. Between the two buildings was an unused in-ground swimming pool. The pool was set back a short way and could easily be missed, as the plants around it tended to hide it from view. However, we stopped to get a better look and it was quite lovely. It had never occurred to me before—a brothel with a swimming pool!

It seemed this smaller building had originally been intended for use as a bathhouse. It was equipped with facilities for both men and women, and was divided into two separate areas. The smaller front area was now used as a waiting room, and the larger back section was where the x-rays were done. Here we encountered more green-robed individuals and once again conversation prevailed and personal stories were told as everyone sat waiting for their turn. By now I was quite sure Marta had amassed more stories and information than even she had ever dreamed possible.

After being x-rayed, I returned with Marta to the large waiting room in the main building. Obviously intended to be a living room, it had a large fireplace and was, even now that it was used as a waiting room, quite inviting. The room was painted the same pale blue as the foyer. Overhead, two large white recessed fans kept the room comfortable, and a door opened invitingly onto a balcony. In front of the fireplace was a large, low, black glass-topped table, and over the fireplace a bulletin board was covered with medical announcements and other pertinent information.

We walked out onto the balcony, an appealing place with a tile floor and white railings, overlooking the city of Tijuana. Due to our location on the hill, the city seemed some distance away. Several neighboring houses could be seen, but we especially admired the house directly below us. It was a sprawling ranch-style home with a tile roof and a beautifully well-kept garden and, as Marta pointed out, an expensive tan car in the carport. While we were enjoying the view, Dennis briefly joined us and explained that the owner of the house we were admiring was the owner of a couple of pharmacies in Tijuana. As a man of means, he is called upon to help members of his family who are not so fortunate, and therefore he also owned the house next door, which he had built to house members of his extended family who came to him for aid. These people repaid him by doing necessary chores such as caring for the garden, etc. Small wonder the place looked so great.

By now, other people had joined us and Dennis related a few interesting details about the Clinic's move across the border. At one time there were seventeen Clinics in the States, the main one located in Dallas. He pointed to a small, very plain building not far from the Clinic and explained that this was their first location when the move across the border was made. Mildred Nelson moved into the second floor of the building (where she still resided) and the Clinic occupied the first floor. For the benefit of those who recently joined us, he explained that Mildred had purchased the present building at auction, and said that a documentary film giving a complete and informative history of the Clinic would be shown; he recommended we all watch it if we had time.

It was hard to believe it was almost noon—the morning had passed so quickly. Marta and I had had conversations and exchanged stories with several people already. We had learned quite a bit about the Clinic, yet standing there on the balcony in the bright sunlight we couldn't help but wonder what the afternoon would bring.

Chapter 5

T.L.C.....?

All pre-exam necessities for me were finished and since fasting was no longer necessary, it was suggested that Marta and I have lunch. Leaving the balcony, we walked back into the garden where a small restaurant was located. The restaurant consisted of one long counter, which had the appearance of an old-fashioned soda fountain. Here, your meal was prepared directly in front of you. The menu was brief—fresh soup, sandwiches, tortillas, fruit juice, etc. There were a few green-robed individuals seated at the counter along with accompanying spouses or friends, and at least one nurse I had seen earlier in the day. After waiting so long to eat, lunch was very welcome, especially the freshly squeezed orange juice.

When we had finished eating we were given a slip of paper showing the amount we owed, and were instructed to put the money into a small box located on a little table near the door. If you had change coming, you merely took whatever that amount happened to be. We were told that there had never been a problem with this system.

Since a large part of the morning was spent compiling results of the miscellaneous tests given to the various patients, it was not surprising for Marta and me to find a few people in the waiting room who had not seen a doctor yet. Our lady friend from northern California entered the room with her daughter and told us that her expectations had been confirmed; she was indeed doing very well. Her daughter, who was overjoyed at her mother's good news, said that while it wasn't always easy to stay on the prescribed diet and follow all the directions given (especially when dining at a restaurant), it was more than worth the effort. It was heartwarming to hear their good news. It would not be long before I would have the opportunity to see a doctor, and I wondered what he would say to me. How wonderful it would be to hear good news...but I realized it was too soon for that as far as I was concerned. And, I had no idea what kind of a diet my friend had been on, or what directions she had followed.

The wait was soon over. Dr. Gutierrez came out and called my name. He said that Marta was welcome to join us, which she did. She, too, was anxious to hear what he would say. He ushered us into his office, a large bright room with big windows, and asked us to sit down. He had a quiet, pleasant manner and we quickly felt comfortable and at ease with him.

I had made arrangements before the trip to obtain the slides of my tumor from the hospital, thinking this would be important, but Dr. Gutierrez said that it would not be necessary to view them. He studied the medical information from the morning (blood work, x-rays, etc.), and then we discussed my medical history. I explained that my surgery was recent, two weeks before, to which he replied that he could see this was the case, because it was still swollen and he believed it must still be quite sore. He asked if I was putting ice on it every day. When I told him I had done this for only one week, he recommended that I resume doing this until the swelling was completely gone. He stressed the importance of resting my right arm, going so far as to suggest that I use my left arm even for small things like opening doors. He explained that it would take time for this surgery to heal and I must do what I could to help it along. I was very surprised by his obviously sincere concern, since my scar was not large and the hospital personnel in the States had treated it so lightly. There is no doubt that Dr. Gutierrez's attitude about my personal comfort impressed me all the more because I had so recently been in the company of doctors whose greatest interest seemed to be mainly (if not solely) performing more surgery. Their patients' physical comfort did not seem to be their prime concern at all.

The checkup with Dr. Gutierrez was very thorough. He said there were several things he would like to see improved before my next blood test. In fact he found a slight infection, not in any way associated with cancer, which he said must be cleared up. It seems that my entire system had been affected by my illness, and although I had not been plagued by physical discomfort, I had noticed for a long time that the whites of my eyes had taken on a darkness that was not natural. I had wondered about the cause of this but had never been able to come to any conclusion, and since no mention of it had been made at the time of my surgery or during previous doctors' visits I had all but forgotten it. Dr. Gutierrez went on to say that although the tumor had been removed, cancer is a very aggressive disease and the instructions he would give me should be followed to the letter every day.

I was to take the Hoxsey tonic on a daily basis, along with vitamins and shark cartilage. The Hoxsey tonic is a concentrated formula containing various and specific amounts of several herbs, including red clover, licorice, burdock, poke root, baberis, cascara, prickly ash bark, buckthorn bark, and potassium iodide. He also prescribed a drug commonly used in the States to treat breast cancer patients. He said I should get the prescription through my regular doctor because it would be cheaper that way, but if I found it impossible to obtain in that manner he would get it for me. My new diet eliminated all red meat and pork. A large variety of fresh fruits and vegetables were to be eaten. Canned foods were to be avoided since they contain too much salt, and all labels should be read to reduce my intake of preservatives as much as possible. Regarding the reading of labels he said, "If you don't know what it is—don't buy it." In addition to the meats, the two main items to be totally eliminated from my diet were tomatoes and vinegar, because the acids in these foods tend to nullify the benefits of the tonic. This restriction made label reading very important, since these ingredients are in so many products. The last thing he said was not to drink the city water when I went back home. I could not help but snicker; was this not what everyone said when one planned a trip across the border?

During this visit, Dr. Gutierrez also questioned me regarding any vitamins and other pills or drugs I had been taking. I explained that the only thing I had been taking was an estrogen-enhancing drug, which had been prescribed years ago and had been taking for several years. He told me never to take this drug again, and I remember him asking, "Why do doctors continue to prescribe this drug when they know there is a real danger?"

Having received this warning, I later checked on the web, where I read that that not only is there a danger of long-term side effects with estrogen replacement therapy, but that even a year-long use increases an otherwise healthy woman's risk of not only cancer but heart attack and stroke as well.

When this drug was first prescribed for me (over ten years before) I recalled that a good friend had also been put on this product by her doctor at approximately the same time. After she had been on the medication for about a year her doctor took her off of it, saying that this was as long as he wanted any one of his patients on it because there were potentially harmful side effects when the drug was taken for prolonged periods. At the time, since I had been told how beneficial it was, I considered her doctor to be wrong and felt he was depriving her of these supposed benefits. And of course, who doesn't want to believe that the doctor they are seeing is "all knowing" and "obviously correct?" Consequently, I continued to take it as instructed. I know now that even long ago it was known that it could be dangerous, resulting in undesirable consequences. Some doctors chose to heed the warning, others to ignore it. It makes one wonder why, after all this time, it is still so widely advertised without adequate warnings. Or is there a warning in fine print at the end of the advertisement that most people ignore or fail to notice? If the possible consequences were brought to their attention, women would be able to judge for themselves if taking it would be worth the risk.

While there is no way of knowing for sure, but with no history of cancer in my family that I know of, my many years of taking this drug could quite conceivably be the cause of my cancer. Dr. Gutierrez undoubtedly felt this way.

Dr. Gutierrez answered all of our questions, never rushing us in any way in spite of the fact that we were with him for a considerable length of time. Marta agreed that the visit was informative and reassuring.

It is obvious that the Hoxsey tonic is the foundation of the Bio-Medical Center's therapy, but it seems so simple—too simple. It consists of herbs and vitamins, along with a very healthy diet. It is very important to follow the recommended way of eating, because how could all the good things in the tonic work if they were constantly undermined by bad diet?

Could it really work? I could think of many doctors who would say it could not. However, here at the Clinic were doctors of medicine. These doctors could prescribe drugs and at times did suggest methods endorsed by the AMA. But whenever possible they choose a less toxic approach, realizing the healing that is possible without surgery or other harsh treatments.

Yes, I thought, I believed it not only could, but that it would work. In the past few hours I had heard many reassuring stories. Eva was no longer the only person I knew of who had benefited from this alternative approach. I knew as I left the office that I would return as requested in three months time, so my progress could be checked.

The inscription on Leona's car came back to me. For me, it was not an overstatement. To me, it was truly T.L.C.

Chapter 6

Unforgettable Goodbyes

The day was coming to an end, but we had a little time before starting our drive back to San Diego to say goodbye to the people we had met.

There was Stanley, a Canadian man approximately 55 years old and wonderfully outgoing, who had come to the Clinic for the first time eight years ago. His mother-in-law had been diagnosed with cancer and she wanted to come to the Clinic. He explained to us how he was totally against the idea, believing it to be a complete waste of time—and more importantly, money—but his mother-in-law was adamant so he and his wife drove down from Canada to be with her. At this time Stanley's wife was suffering greatly from asthma, a fact that was noticed by one of the doctors after they had arrived at the Clinic. This doctor suggested that as long as she was here, why not talk to someone about her asthma to see if something could be done? Again Stanley said he indicated his strong disapproval, saying the doctors were just a bunch of quacks. His wife however, against his wishes, decided to see if her condition could be improved in any way. She saw a doctor and was given instructions, along with a certain herbal prescription to take. She was told that after taking the herbal prescription for approximately six months (as it would take some time for her condition to improve) she would be much better.

Stanley said he was totally dubious, doubting every word, especially since his wife's asthma was so severe that there were days she had a hard time simply getting out of bed. But his wife went home and followed all the advice she had been given and six months later, almost to the day, her asthma was gone. Not just better, he said, but gone. And unbelievably, since that time she has been fine. After telling us about his wife he then said, "That is my wife sitting over there knitting, and that is my mother-in-law next to her, back for a checkup." It was clear his opinion of the Bio-Medical Center had taken a dramatic turn.

The cowboy in the group, who happened to be from (where else?) Texas, told us he took tour groups out on horseback, sometimes for days at a time. It was difficult for him to stay on his recommended diet and take the tonic as instructed at these times, but knowing how important it was he did his best. He explained that he had a tumor behind one eye, which he was hopeful of totally shrinking in order to keep his eye. He was back for a checkup and was confident and upbeat, and I could well imagine this slim, wiry man in control—not only of a group of tourists on horseback, but also of his own health.

Bob, a truck driver from Colorado, was also back for a checkup, and when he realized it was our first visit he wanted us to hear his story. He said that when his doctor (at home) informed him that he had cancer, the doctor wasted no time getting him into the hospital. This almost immediate and unexpected event left Bob terrified. He said he hardly had a moment to think things through—he just followed orders. Surgery was performed immediately, and he said his only recollection is of how sick he was. He could not get out of bed; he could only lay watching fluids drip into his arm. He resolved that he would never allow anyone to put him in such a situation again. As soon as he was physically able, he came to the Clinic.

While talking to Bob, one of our car companions (the lady returning for her 17th visit) approached and asked Bob, "Don't I know you?" Bob said yes, he remembered seeing her on his last visit. She told him how wonderful he looked, exclaiming it was not just because his hair had grown back in but that he looked like a whole new person. Bob replied that he did indeed feel like a new person, and that he was doing great. Knowing what he had been through, it was heartening to see him in such high spirits and good health.

The last people we met during that first visit were a young couple, obviously pleased at the end of the day. They joyously reported that they had received some excellent news. The wife had some kind of an abdominal tumor, which had been diagnosed some months before. She had opted not to have surgery, but came to the Clinic instead. X-rays now showed that the tumor was shrinking. This was yet another of the many personal and detailed stories Marta and I collected. But the simplest, most heartfelt comment we overheard about the Clinic that day was: "It takes the fear out." I don't think there is any better way to describe the atmosphere at the Clinic. There may be other diseases that claim more lives, but cancer is by far the one that conjures up the most fear. Who has not heard of the pain, the unpleasant medical procedures, and the surgeries? All too often the outcome is fatal. Everyone knows someone who did not make it.

Undoubtedly there are people who come to the Clinic—perhaps too late, or for reasons I cannot imagine— who cannot be helped, but this was very definitely not the case on this day of my first visit.

Finally, at the end of the day, I thought once again of Bonny and our long-ago conversation. I recalled the reassuring feeling I had when I left Dr. West's office knowing I would come here. But I also remembered the butterflies in my stomach when I first arrived in San Diego, wondering what was ahead for me. I could not help but wonder about the different circumstances and avenues that brought so many people from all walks of life to this place. Everyone had an interesting story to tell.

Leaving Mexico was quite different than arriving. As Leona's car approached the border, we found ourselves at the end of a long line of vehicles. Now the border guards were not so indifferent! Each car was stopped and the people asked about their citizenship, along with, "what did you buy?," "what do you have in the car that you are bringing back?," etc. It made for a long wait but then, the entire day had been so much more gratifying than I had expected. Like me, I believe everyone in the car was returning to San Diego with positive thoughts.

Chapter 7

Reactions

It all seemed quite simple. Once I returned home, I would explain to family and doctors that I had decided to follow the method prescribed at the Bio-Medical Center. I would be taking the tonic four times daily and would restrict my diet by avoiding certain foods that counteract the herbs in the tonic. I would also eat the healthy foods they recommended, and take certain vitamins.

Never did I expect the responses I received.

My husband and son could not believe that my eyes had not been opened to the ludicrousness of the entire idea after actually being in Mexico. Calls arrived from concerned relatives as well, all echoing the same thoughts. I know everyone had my best interests at heart, but I felt strongly about my decision. And because Marta had spoken to patients and asked questions, she could see the positive side of what I was doing. Fortunately I had this one voice of approval.

When I told my surgeon, Dr. West, that I would be returning to the Clinic in three months, the news was received as though I had made a decision to go against the commands of the most high. The attitudes of the nursing staff, too, once they were aware of my plans, quietly implied that I would surely be sorry. How could I ignore the advice of some of the finest doctors in the state? It was impossible for them to fathom. My statements, opinions, feelings and desires were not to be considered, or even listened to. In their eyes, apparently only what the doctor suggested was valid. Dr. West did, however, agree to prescribe the drug Dr. Gutierrez recommended I take. This was the only prescription drug advised for me at the Clinic. Dr. West confirmed the fact that this was indeed a popular and widely prescribed drug in the States for breast cancer patients. One he prescribed for his own patients.

In spite of these reactions I changed my eating habits, stayed on the tonic, and attempted to not be overwhelmed by all the negative comments I was continually hearing. Due to these initial responses, I decided not to reveal my illness or my plans to friends or coworkers. I also did not want to hear any "poor Marie" comments or to have the feeling that anyone was guarding their statements while talking to me. In addition to this, everything was new to me and very personal, and as the days went by and I heard more of the same responses from out-of-state family members who had been told the news, it confirmed the fact that my decision to withhold the information at this time was a wise one.

During the next three months I followed Dr. Gutierrez's instructions. I resumed the ice packs, using my arm as little as possible until the swelling was totally gone. Even after the swelling receded I was still very sore, so it was quite some time before I was using my arm normally again. Given the fact that my surgery was minor, I wondered how long the discomfort would have lasted if I had gone through with the additional surgery the doctors had wanted to perform. Changing my eating habits, however, was not a dramatic obstacle, possibly easier for me than for some people since I had never been a "fast food junkie." During this period of time I felt as though my entire body was being cleansed, and the whites of my eyes lost the yellowish appearance they once had.

Probably the most difficult thing for me to give up was coffee. At work each morning I had always had a cup (or possibly two), and I was sure someone would pick up on my sudden lack of interest in my morning coffee. In fact, upon my return to work it was a rare day when someone did not ask me if I'd like a cup, my usual answer being, "a little later thank you" or something along that line. Surprisingly, without my ever saying I had given it up, no one noticed that I had stopped drinking coffee. In fact, as it turned out, I went for two entire years without drinking a cup, and yet the comments about the Scandinavians and coffee never ceased. "No detective work going on in this police department," I thought.

When I returned to the Clinic in December for my three-month checkup, I found that my blood test had improved greatly and all was going well. The infection that was discovered on my first trip had cleared up. This was great news and I was truly grateful to everyone at the Clinic, and for my good fortune to be able to come to such a place. The doctor at the Clinic would have liked me to return again in another three months time, but since I was progressing nicely and they realized it was a long trip for me, the time until my next visit was extended to six months. It was requested that I see my own doctor after three months for another blood test, and that I have the results sent to the Clinic. I agreed to do this. Before leaving the Clinic I was given a six-month supply of tonic, and instructed to continue taking the vitamins, stay on the diet, and keep taking the prescribed medication.

On this trip, knowing we would only be at the Clinic for one day, we decided to stay in San Diego for a couple of days longer in order to see a little of the city before returning home. Since it was the middle of December, San Diego was all decked out for Christmas, looking entirely different than Massachusetts looks at this time of the year. Coming from a place where Christmas is usually a time of snow and ice, seeing lights strung around palm trees and cactus plants was a unique experience. Flowers bloomed everywhere, seeming somewhat out of place when displayed alongside Santas and Christmas angels. But then, winter doesn't really come to southern California. We did, however, see a beautiful Christmas tree in the lobby at the Hotel Del, one of the places we visited before going back home. It was a lovely trip and we almost forgot that the original reason we had come was for my checkup.

Chapter 8

The Start of an Interesting and Unusual Year

In January I was scheduled for a regular checkup with my primary care physician, Dr. Simms. Dr. Simms had of course been informed that I had gone to the Bio-Medical Center and I wondered how she would react, but since everything was going so well for me I was confident that the visit would be positive.

It was an interesting session because she asked to have a student sit in, a request that I complied with. After the examination was complete, and it was determined that she could find nothing wrong, the doctor proceeded to tell me that I was to begin the standard treatment for cancer patients. She had no regard for any treatment other than that which she had been taught, and the fact that I was doing well at the moment meant nothing to her. I know she felt her instructions were not only correct, but that they should be followed to the letter, and by no means questioned by her patient. "But," I asserted, "it is my choice to continue with the procedures as outlined at the Clinic." She was obviously very unhappy with me; it had to be a blow to her professional pride not to be able to convince a patient regarding treatment in front of a student. However, I strongly felt (and still feel) it is the right of every person (after exploring all of their options) to agree or disagree with treatment suggested by a doctor, and to be allowed to make his or her individual decision. Needless to say, the session did not end on a very positive note.

Shortly after the appointment with Dr. Simms, she sent me a letter stating that she was very busy and was taking on additional responsibilities, so she was reducing the number of patients in her care. I was to look for another doctor.

I checked the list of available female doctors, asked a few acquaintances associated with hospitals or the medical profession whom they might recommend, and finally selected a new primary care physician, Dr. Roberts. Since I had told Dr. West I would remain in contact with him, I informed him of my new primary care physician.

My appointment with Dr. Roberts was scheduled for a short time later, but needless to say I was concerned about how this first meeting with my new primary care physician would play out, and indeed it was a little bizarre.

As she sat talking to me, she asked for more and more information. I answered her questions, told her I had recently been to the Clinic (for my second visit), was staying on my diet, taking vitamins and the herbal tonic, and taking the drug suggested at the Clinic but prescribed by Dr. West. Everything I said seemed new to her, so I finally said, "All of this information is in my folder, along with an article about the Clinic. I gave all of it to my previous primary care physician." Dr. Roberts said that no such information was in my folder, and then stated it had probably been removed and placed in the archives before the folder was transferred to her. I felt it was extremely strange that anything should be removed, and it seemed to anger her because she immediately made a telephone call asking to have all information that had been removed sent to her. Although Dr. Roberts could find nothing wrong with me, which I felt was a positive sign, her attitude made it seem questionable. She was not pleased to hear that I had refused further surgery, which she felt should still be done, and she could not understand why I was reluctant to have radiation. Our parting was like an uneasy truce.

Apparently what she found in the archives was not to her liking, because it was not long after this that I received a letter stating that she had to cut back on her patient load, and that since I was one of her newest patients I was to look for another primary care physician. Not following directions is apparently a grievous sin, not easily forgiven, and having something in your medical records that states you left the country and are following the advice of doctors in Tijuana, Mexico is unthinkable. I wondered how many other people returning from the Clinic to their own doctors in this country ran into similar situations. It was hard to imagine that I was the only one.

Fortunately, Dr. West had arranged for the blood test I needed for the Clinic, and I could pick up a copy of the results. Being unable to come on the scheduled day I called to change it, and after the nurse realized whom she was talking to she became quite terse regarding my need for the blood work. She said, "But you are not doing anything." Knowing she had my records in front of her, and that she knew exactly what I was doing, I felt no need to explain except to say, "I am doing something." "Well," she said, "this is highly irregular," to which I replied, "I'm well aware of that." It again made me wonder how long it would be before people would simply accept my decision and what I was doing (or not doing as the case might be, depending on how they looked at it). At any rate I finally received the results of the blood work and sent it to the Clinic.

Of course, this left me once again with the chore of finding a new primary care physician. Again I scoured the list of available female doctors, hoping this would be the last time it would be necessary. I selected a Dr. Martin, since a friend recommend her and I liked what I heard. However, my first appointment with her wouldn't be until after my next visit to the Clinic.

Chapter 9

The Following Summer at the Clinic

The following summer our trip to the Clinic introduced us to some very interesting people. Marta once again accompanied me, and again because she had the opportunity to converse while I was having tests or seeing the doctor, we met quite a few people.

We met a man and his wife who were both back for three-month checkups. They both had Lupus and said that there were many such cases in their area back home. It was believed that this was due to toxic waste products that had been buried where they lived several years before. They were so impressed with the Clinic that this time they brought their teenaged daughter with them. The daughter had also donned the familiar green robe we all wore, so although I do not know her medical background, it was obvious she was being checked along with her parents.

We met three sisters from northern California, the two younger sisters accompanying the eldest one, who had cancer. They had discussed coming to the Clinic months before but, having doctors in the family, they were strongly advised against the trip. Now that the family doctors had done all they felt could be done (and for all intents and purposes had given up) they finally agreed that she could come if she really wanted to. As Marta and I talked to the two accompanying sisters while the oldest was with the doctor, they expressed their concern that they may have waited too long. Marta and I found in later trips to the Clinic that all too often anyone with medical people in the family was more than likely there as a last resort. This was apparently such a case.

Ironically, we later spoke to a man who told us about a friend who'd run into his hometown doctor at the Clinic. When his friend asked the doctor what he was doing at the Bio-Medical Center, the doctor said he was accompanying his wife, who insisted on coming.

We also met a lovely lady from Australia. We did not have a chance to hear her story, but Dennis told us that the Clinic had quite a few patients from "Down Under." Several months earlier, a man from Australia had come and was so pleased with his experience that he wanted others to know about it. He had a connection of some kind with the Australian television industry and had information about the Clinic broadcast in that country. He arranged for groups of approximately fifty people at a time to fly to the States and then travel by bus to the Clinic. Dennis said that such a group had arrived recently, making for a very busy day.

It was also on this visit that I met Kippie, who traveled to the Clinic from northern California. Since then we've had the opportunity to meet her mother, who lives in the San Diego area, and also to occasionally spend time visiting with Kippie while we are in the city. She remains a friend to this day.

Chapter 10

Traveling into Year Two

It was hard to believe that the better part of a year had passed since my first visit to the Clinic. However, my silence continued in spite of the good reports regarding my health and the fact that I had never felt better. But it was a different story with Marta. She worked at a bank, and was telling customers who came in relating concern about a friend or relative with cancer about the Clinic. She handed out copies of a magazine article about the Clinic and relayed as much verbal information as possible. She also gave out my telephone number in case they would like to talk to me, and while I was otherwise silent I was very happy to talk to these people.

At about this time, Marta told me that when we first went to San Diego and the Clinic, her father had instructed her to pick up on all the adverse information possible, and to talk me out of this nonsense. Little did he know she was to become a very outspoken advertisement for the place.

It seemed, however, after returning from California, that my trips to various doctors' offices were endless. It was time for my scheduled annual appointment with Dr. West, and shortly after that I would be meeting with Dr. Martin who, I hoped, would be my permanent primary care physician.

Upon my arrival at Dr. West's office, I gave my name at the desk and turned to find a seat. Almost immediately I overheard a voice whisper loudly, "There she is, she's here." Turning, I saw a face peer around the corner to get a look at what kind of a person actually goes to Mexico for alternative cancer treatments. I felt others staring, too, but I doubt I was what they expected to see. Why—I was quite ordinary looking—they might even pass me on the street never suspecting I could be capable of such unconventional behavior! However, all the sudden interest in me that day had it's own small reward. I had no sooner entered the waiting room and sat down than my name was called. It was the shortest wait I ever had in a doctor's office.

My meeting with Dr. West was brief. He seemed hesitant to ask questions about the Bio-Medical Center, even though I felt he really wanted to know more about the place. I had given him information about the Clinic, and although I'm sure he had unanswered thoughts and questions, nothing of any consequence was asked. My feeling was that he was surprised I was doing so well. He asked what I would do if it were suddenly apparent that I had another tumor and needed to have it removed. I told him that quite honestly I would have to give such a situation a great deal of thought, as I had now been exposed to other treatment possibilities and felt that surgery might not always be the best or the only option. He may not have liked what I said, but he did say he could appreciate the fact that "quality of life" was so important to me. I feel that to live in pain or constantly feel sick is not living. Knowing I had received a letter from Dr. Simms, he asked how I liked my new primary care person, Dr. Roberts. He found it hard to believe that I had also received a letter from her. I said I had selected a new doctor, Dr. Martin (whom he knew) but because I had not met her yet, I did not know how things would go. I told him that I would return to see him again in another year, adding: "Don't expect me to be sick." We both smiled, and while we were miles apart in a lot of ways, it was a good visit and I had every intention of keeping my next appointment with him.

When the day finally came to meet Dr. Martin I was, to say the least, a bit unnerved. More than anything else at that moment I hoped this first visit would not be my last.

As it turned out, meeting Dr. Martin was a pleasant surprise. We started out on somewhat shaky ground, because she found my blood pressure was elevated and said it looked to her like I should be on medication. I explained that it was no doubt due to my nervousness about the visit, since my blood pressure has always been fine in the past. She suggested that I return to her office every day for the next week or two to have it checked. I explained to her that this wasn't convenient for me, but that I was sure one of the paramedics who worked with me at the police station would be willing to take it for several days. She said that this would be acceptable, and I could mail the results to her.

Dr. Martin then asked me about the Bio-Medical Clinic. She said she had read all the articles in my folder (this time they had not been removed), and then told me that Dr. West had written her a letter regarding my unorthodox course of action. While she did not let me read the letter, she quoted it as saying: "I don't know why she is doing so well, but she is" and: "I can find no reoccurrence or any sign of cancer." This was followed by something to the effect of: "Let her continue whatever she is doing." It made me wonder at that moment if, without the letter, her attitude might have been different. However, the rest of the visit went well, so I had no desire to question her. She said that I looked great and she was content to have me continue with my special diet and whatever else I was doing. She then told me she would be moving to a new office in the fall and hoped I would continue to see her at this new location. This I would be more than glad to do. I was delighted to finally find a doctor I felt I could talk to.

As promised, I had the paramedics take my blood pressure for approximately two weeks, whenever they were not out on a call or otherwise tied up. After taking it a few times one of the paramedics said, "I think there's a story behind this," and another said he wished his blood pressure was comparable to mine. I just explained that it was my doctor's request. The results were mailed, and apparently added to my folder. Hearing nothing further, I assumed medication was not necessary after all.

Looking back, it is hard to believe it took me so long to find a doctor I could actually talk to, and it is equally difficult to believe some of the situations I encountered. I would never have thought it all possible if it had not actually happened to me.

At this time I started telling a few (very few) people about my alternative procedures and, in spite of the fact that I was doing well, most of them could not understand my decision to deviate from the traditional route of chemo, radiation, etc. Everyone was familiar with friends or family who had suffered—some, in spite of their suffering, succumbing to the disease. Even so, the consensus seemed to be that these patients had all done things the right way, and that was the only way to go. They had followed their doctors' advice and had done everything that could possibly be done. Somehow, it seemed I was doing something wrong. I did not appear sick or unhealthy, but they were sure either it would not last, or I was initially misdiagnosed, or maybe I was just the one exceptionally lucky person—the unusual case. In fact, one of my very good friends made the statement that I would probably have been alright anyway, whether I had gone to the Clinic or not. To this friend I could only answer that if, on the other hand, I had followed the advice of the doctors in the states, I would in all probability now be minus a breast and my lymph nodes; then everyone would no doubt be saying I was saved thanks to modern medicine. I am quite certain that more than one of my friends mentioned my alternative method to their doctors, only to have their opinions confirmed that indeed I was the exception. Their doctors no doubt stated that the recommendations of the AMA were the only intelligent way to go. This attitude reminded me of some churches that proclaim there is only one way to God—namely, theirs. But I believe there is more than one way to God, and in the treatment of cancer I believe there is also more than one way. Desperately, I wanted to say: "Please allow the rusted padlocks of your mind to break open, allowing fresh awareness and possibilities to rush in. Until you do, you will never know what wonders you may encounter."

At work, however, for the most part I remained quiet about what I was doing. I never missed a day, so no one had any suspicion of what had transpired in my life. Also, because I enjoy my job and the people I work with very much, and realizing how most people react to the word cancer, I did not want to create an uncomfortable atmosphere. It seemed ironic that when I first heard about the Clinic so long ago, I thought the news was wonderful. Now it seemed that very few people shared my views. Was it due to a fear of going against the norm, even when the alternative was so promising? Was it always necessary to be a follower, never even taking the time to look into other options? I never considered myself a bold person, but I always felt I had the right to question. I was coming to realize that few people follow their feelings, even those deep within themselves. It seems this is mostly because they do not want to be different, or in any way stand apart from the crowd. Not making waves seems to be the way to go—at any cost.

During the summer of the second year after my diagnosis, I returned to the Clinic and found that all was still going well. I was told taking the shark cartilage was now optional. The doctor now suggested that I drink yew bark tea every day. It was known that the yew contained cancer-resisting qualities, and they felt it would add to the benefits already supplied by the tonic. Fortunately, I was able to obtain the tea at the Clinic at a very reasonable cost. During this visit I was also told that an occasional cup of coffee would be fine. I welcomed this news, not just because I could enjoy my morning coffee again, but because it was a sign that I was truly on the right track. I'm certain there are times when individuals from the Clinic are not able to follow their prescribed diets to the letter (when eating out, for example), but knowing how important it is, everyone would surely do their best. I had gone without one single cup of coffee for months, and now the thought of going to work and pouring myself a cup felt strange. The day I went to the office and helped myself to a cup for the first time in two years, I thought someone would surely say something, but no one had even noticed my abstinence. As far as they were concerned, I was just having my usual morning coffee. As a matter of fact, it wasn't too long before I even heard comments such as: "You know, Marie, drinking too much coffee isn't good for you!"

Part 2

Reflection

Chapter 1

Looking Back

As I write this chapter, almost eight years have passed since my first trip to the Bio-Medical Center. My grandsons are no longer babies. Joe has just turned twelve and Jake will soon be ten. This is the most evident and constant reminder of how much time has passed. I am still working as a secretary at the Holden Police Department, but the years have brought changes. Three officers have retired, along with the Chief, and we have acquired several new officers, filling both full time and part time positions. My current boss (the new Chief) is wonderfully easy to work for. As an avid runner he has helped inspire others, and even though our department is not large, our officers have placed well in competitive races. Along with being recognized for our physical fitness program, the department is well known for our very competent detective and our work in Community Policing. In fact, the Department received much attention when it was selected the "New England Police Department of the Year" for 2001. Happily, the friendly atmosphere continues as before, making it a very pleasant place to work.

With regard to my health, as well, I cannot help but reflect on all that has transpired. The events and incidents have been many. Often they have been humorous, sometimes frustrating, and often I have been left with the feeling that I'm truly on my own and I'd better make the best of it. Several of the experiences involved visits to doctors' offices, and others came about when new people unexpectedly entered my life. But whatever else the experiences may have been, they were always interesting, and I am grateful for what they have taught me.

All along I knew I had gathered remarkable information but was not sharing it with others. I felt I was purposefully remaining in a closet, but knowing that most people I dealt with on a day-to-day basis would be diametrically opposed to what I was doing, I remained quiet. I shared my story with relatively few people and, with the exception of a few friends, no one I worked with or associated with were aware that my yearly jaunts to San Diego included a trip to Tijuana.

I felt that once my doctors realized I was doing well and intended to stay on the Hoxsey therapy and, as I said before, since most people never knew what I was doing in the first place, my thought was that I would simply fall into a comfortable and uneventful routine. This, however, was not to be the case.

During my first year or two on the Hoxsey therapy, I clearly remember—more than once—telling nurses or doctors about my "unusual" cancer treatments. I told them about the patients I had met at the Clinic and how well things seemed to go for so many. Their standard response at that time was: "Maybe they did these things for other people, but what are they doing for you?." Now, several years later, when they look at me and find nothing wrong with me, the statement is something like: "Sure, they helped you, but what have they done for anyone else?." All I can say is that perhaps in time people will be more open-minded.

It seems that most of the time when alternative procedures are followed and picked up by the media, the story involves a show business figure, or someone equally well known. With this in mind, Marta and I once asked Dennis about such persons while we were at the Clinic. Dennis told us that phone calls from well known personalities were not infrequent, but when the person was told the reasonable rates and probably also a little about the (seemingly) simple treatment, they never contacted the Clinic again. There is also no doubt that the very restricted diet would not appeal to persons used to lifestyles of luxury, without restrictive guidelines. It is not unreasonable to assume that these people ended up at a much more expensive place, probably staying for prolonged periods of time. Unfortunately, it is also the rationale of all too many Americans that "the more it costs, the better it is."

It is also far more appealing to place the responsibility of getting better on someone else—not making it too personal. The profusion of ads on television and the many books written about losing weight, improving the physique, etc. all testify to the fact that a great many people do not have the discipline to stay on one program or plan. If they hear of something new that sounds easier, faster or just plain better, they are quick to disregard the old plan and embrace the new.

Without a doubt, media attention is quick, intense, and usually negative with regard to any unconventional approach to treating serious illness. I have often wondered if the focus would be more positive if someone famous experienced the same healing results that so many patients at the Clinic have enjoyed. Not long ago, the popular celebrity Suzanne Somers was in the news, criticized for seeking non-traditional approaches to treating her breast cancer. Since she is often in the limelight, it will be most interesting to observe the reactions of the media and her other critics if the path she chooses leads her back to good health—as I hope and pray it will. I also wondered if, as time went on, the doctors in the States that I was seeing regularly would look positively on my approach to wellness or if, in spite of it, my continuing good health would be chalked up to something else. Learned answers die slow deaths.

As promised, I continued to see Dr. West once a year. Somehow I felt these visits were just as important to my primary care physician Dr. Martin as they were to me, because she always asked about them. Perhaps because my medical treatment was unconventional and Dr. West held a position of authority at the hospital, she found it comforting to know she had his approval (which the letter he had sent confirmed). Fortunately my visits with both doctors were comfortable and without discord of any kind. In the rare cases when uncomfortable situations did arise, it usually involved a new assistant, intern, or resident doctor.

I continued to feel, during my visits with Dr. West, that the brochures I'd given him and comments I made did not satisfy his curiosity about the Clinic, but his professional position kept him from asking questions. He was a man others came to when they had questions, so it was not comfortable for him to seek additional information or answers from a patient. However, after the Clinic suggested I add yew bark tea to my daily routine, I mentioned it to Dr. West and he was very interested in it. I realized his curiosity was because he was aware that the AMA was conducting research on the yew tree, which they felt had certain cancer-fighting properties; I knew his unexpected interest in the tea in no way meant he was beginning to accept my full course of treatment at the Clinic.

To my surprise he was actually interested in obtaining some of the tea and asked me where I got it. I told him I had purchased it at the Clinic, remembered that it came from someplace in Mexico, and that I would look at the address on the package. Knowing full well that Dr. West was not likely to suggest that his patients drink this tea, my thought was that it must be for a member of his family, or perhaps a close friend. I told Dr. West that the tea alone was not enough to make a difference, reminding him that I was just taking it as a supplement (the tonic being the important item), but I would be glad to send the information to him. When I returned home I checked and found that this package of tea—it was the second I had received at the Clinic—was from Montana, not Mexico as the first package had been. I sent Dr. West a note with the address, included instructions about how long to boil it, and suggested sweetening it with honey. Several weeks later I read an article in the paper about a doctor from Dr. West's hospital who had died of cancer. The article was quite long, recognizing the doctor for continuing to treat cancer patients even as she suffered from the disease herself. Quite possibly, I thought, she was the recipient of the yew bark tea purchased by Dr. West.

During my yearly visits with Dr. West, someone else (a nurse or resident/intern) usually spoke with me first and it seemed they loved to point out to Dr. West that they had possibly discovered a new cancer growth. This would, of course, prove the grave mistake I was making by refusing surgery, chemotherapy and radiation.

I remember one intern clearly. When Dr. West entered the examining room, the intern informed him that she had detected a lump. Dr. West examined the area and asked if it was all right to do a needle biopsy to determine if it was cancerous. I was confident this was not the case and was ready to say "no," but looking at the intern I knew she would take this as proof that I did not want to face the truth, so I told him to go ahead "as long as it would not be painful." He said it wouldn't be, which was not exactly true, but it was not altogether bad, either. The lump was discovered to be a fatty cell of some sort, which made me comment that I thought this was a part of the body where one should have some fat. I do not like to say the intern was disappointed, but looking at her I believe she was not exactly pleased that she had not discovered something more serious to validate her opinions.

Only twice do I recall members of the medical profession being sincerely interested in the treatment I was pursuing. Both were nurses, who had obviously read all of the information in my folder before I met them. Both wanted to know as much as possible about the Clinic and it's recommendations. Perhaps the reason for their open-mindedness was that a substantial amount of time had passed since my diagnosis, and it was evident that my health was good. Both were very interested in my diet and felt strongly that the medical profession routinely overlooks diet as it relates to cancer, especially when working with patients on an individual basis. They also asked about the vitamins and tonic I took daily. The first nurse told me she had taken her young daughter to an herbalist when she felt the treatment plan outlined by the pediatrician was not in the best interest of the child. The herbalist had helped the child significantly, without following the drastic course of action the pediatrician had recommended. She stated that she felt there was much to be learned about herbs and other alternatives. The second nurse, whom I talked to for a considerable length of time said, "You should write a book." I replied that the idea had crossed my mind.

More often than not, however, the reactions of medical personnel were similar to those of another nurse I encountered. She had been at the hospital prior to my surgery, so she knew Dr. West was my doctor. She happened to come into his waiting room when I was there for one of my annual visits. She stopped to say hello and ask how things were going, since she had not seen me since my surgery. I had met her for the first time when I was at the hospital for my pre-surgery exam, and she had been especially thoughtful and caring. I greatly appreciated this, because it seemed that the other hospital personnel failed to realize that a person does not get operated on every day, so it might be a little unnerving.

Because I had these fond memories of her, I was happy for the chance to talk to her as I waited for my appointment with Dr. West. She sat down beside me and I told her I was feeling fine. I then proceeded to tell her that I had chosen an alternative approach and was not doing the traditional radiation, chemo, or additional surgery. Her reaction was one of total disbelief. She was clearly shocked as she exclaimed, "What will Dr. West say?" When I told her he was fully aware of my decision, it was obvious that she did not believe he really knew—that she felt he would never put up with anything as bizarre as a patient going to Mexico for treatment. She then began to act as though the sooner she left and was not seen with me, the better off she'd be. After all, we are known by the company we keep—and who knows what it might do to her reputation to be seen with someone like me?

One intern at the hospital felt she knew, without a doubt, the real reason for my current good health. She was not only an enthusiastic devotee of physical fitness but had also read books about the success of the mind-body connection over disease. She was amazed that I had not read any similar books. She felt strongly it was my attitude and diet that had made me well; the Hoxsey tonic had nothing to do with it. I told her that although I felt physical fitness and attitude are very important and can indeed make a difference in healing when one becomes sick, I could not give attitude and fitness full credit for my improvement and continued good health. I truly thought that as someone so receptive to mind-body theories, she would be eager to look into my treatment further and find out a little more about it. Her total dismissal of the Hoxsey treatment as the core of my well-being mystified me.

While the cost of going to the Clinic had never come up in any of my conversations with Dr. Martin or Dr. West, it became increasingly obvious that Dr. Martin assumed it was very expensive. ("Paying too much attention to TV reports about high-profile people," I thought to myself). She knew that Marta and I traveled to San Diego each year, and that I returned to the Clinic each time for a checkup. Since I could tell she was curious about the cost, I finally asked, "Would you like to know how much I paid the last time I went?" I then proceeded to tell her exactly what the charges had been, along with details about what the day was like—blood work, urinalysis, x-rays, physical, etc. I also mentioned the fact that one is never rushed when speaking with a doctor. I explained that the first visit for most patients was probably the most expensive due to additional testing, the initial cost of the tonic, etc., but the cost of checkups was far below what anyone in the States could imagine. Years ago, Mr. Hoxsey had promised his father that he would keep the cost within the reach of the general public, and that long-ago promise still holds true to this day. As a result, the total amount I paid for my full course of treatment was very reasonable, for which I was very grateful. Dr. Martin was obviously surprised and impressed that they were able to keep costs to a minimum, observing a bit wryly that medical facilities here in the States might learn something from their neighbors South of the Border.

Possibly the single most memorable, and most humorous, moment I can remember happened in Dr. Martin's waiting room. Before my appointment that day, Dr. Martin had apparently told her assistant that I would be coming in, and no doubt my background was discussed and was of interest to her. No one was in the waiting room when I arrived, but a few minutes later a couple came in and sat on the other side of the room. The man looked like a rough motorcycle rider. He was dressed completely in leather, with a heavy chain hanging from his belt. His hair was long, and he sported several tattoos. The woman who accompanied him was also somewhat of a character. Her hair was bleached blonde, with noticeable dark roots. She wore the brightest pink sweatpants I ever saw, running shoes, and a tee shirt with something written on it in large letters. She also wore a number of bracelets and earrings; with all that jewelry on her wrists and ears, she had the look of a gypsy (not that gypsies usually wear pink or bleach their hair). The three of us all sat, quietly reading magazines. When Dr. Martin's assistant entered the room, she walked towards the couple and said "Marie?" When I responded by getting up and walking towards her while the woman in pink remained seated, the expression on the assistant's face became incredulous. It was obvious that she had already decided for herself which one of us was Marie, and could not believe that a grandmotherly person like myself was the one going to Mexico. Even as I left the doctor's office that day, she stared after me in disbelief. I have smiled to myself many times when I've recalled that moment.

As time went by, however, I found Dr. Martin to be an exceptional primary care physician, always willing to listen to me and validate my concerns. Fortunate are those who find a doctor with these qualities. While Dr. Martin always takes steps to ensure my overall well-being, she has the willingness and ability to accept the fact that my cancer was cured by the Hoxsey tonic and a healthy diet while in her care, and not by procedures accepted by the AMA. (It is important to note here that I took the tonic for six years, which is about average for most patients. The tonic needs time to first detoxify the body and then build up the immune system, allowing the body to heal itself and return to normal). Unfortunately there are some doctors who find it impossible to be so open-minded. There are also too many who want to personally exact the esteem and credit for a patient's good health or cure. They would find it doubly difficult to admit a successful outcome—or even improvement—from unconventional means.

At my third yearly visit to the Clinic, Dr. Gutierrez took me off the prescription drug he prescribed on my first visit, and he replaced it with a similar product that was herbal instead of prescription. Dr. West, who had always been very kind about prescribing this drug for me, could not understand why I should not continue as before, saying he had patients who had been on it for as long as ten years. I told him that the Clinic doctors said they did not like a patient on it for more than three years and that was why I was to now take the herbal product. When I looked this product up on a web site, I found that while the benefits of the drug are great and it can be a life saver, it does have side effects. Studies have found that there was a two- to three-fold increase in both uterine cancer and blood clots in women who took it. Surely, since the Clinic was no doubt well aware of the dangers associated with long-term use, it was prudent to replace it with an herbal product long before the possibilities of these adverse conditions should arise. I remained on the herbal product for approximately two years. One would only hope that undesirable side effects (no matter how small) are explained to each patient by their doctor. In my opinion, no one should take medication of any kind without full knowledge of it's capabilities, both beneficial and harmful. Perhaps if I had known the side effects of the estrogen-enhancing drug that was prescribed for me, I would not have taken it for as long as I did, especially since I knew my friend's doctor had taken her off the product after a year. Then, if I had continued to take it in spite of this knowledge, the choice would have been mine.

Approximately three years after my surgery, the hospital where it was performed sent me a questionnaire. Accompanied by a standard form letter, it was apparently sent to all of their breast cancer patients. The letter stated that the purpose of the questionnaire was to compile statistics on how their former patients were doing. They were collecting the information in order to compare the long-term health of patients depending on medications they had taken, and the possible influence of eating habits. There were several questions asked, but the only one I noticed at the time was if an estrogen-enhancing drug was being taken, specifying the name of the drug. It was the same product I was asked about during my post-surgery interview. The questionnaire struck me as rather cold and insensitive and I threw it away.

Shortly thereafter I received a duplicate questionnaire; I suppose the assumption was that since they received no reply, I had not received the first one. This time I returned the form, but the only notation I made on it was regarding the estrogen-enhancing drug question. I wrote that there appeared to be an oversight on the questionnaire with regard to that question. Surely it should have included a statement that estrogen-enhancing drugs could be detrimental to one's health, and although the hospital should know better than anyone else that there was a real danger in taking this product, no such warning was on the form. To this day I have never received another questionnaire, and never did I receive an answer to the note I sent. It seemed that the compiling of information for statistical purposes was more important than protecting patients. How many more years have to pass and how many more patients have to die—used as guinea pigs—before the medical profession is ready to admit that taking such a drug might not be a good idea?

Shortly after receiving the questionnaires, I received an invitation to subscribe to a health magazine, along with the first issue free-of-charge. It looked like a wonderful magazine, full of good advice with regard to diet and so-forth. Upon opening the magazine however, within the first few pages, I noticed a two-page ad for this same estrogen-enhancing drug. I found this unbelievable. I sent a note to the magazine, thanking them for the issue but stating that I was not at all interested in subscribing. When a "health" magazine endorses such a product, it makes me wonder what other ads are included which are not only questionable but not in their readers' best interest. I never heard from them again. Obviously, the two-page ad was very expensive. While I would like to believe that magazines professing health would not be tempted to accept ads from large companies (whose primary interest is their profitability), I'm afraid money speaks very loudly.

I know everyone has heard of, or is well aware of Guardian Angels—spirit guides that sometimes forewarn us of danger, or possibly send messages about events that have already taken place or are about to happen. Some people feel the presence of this being very strongly, and I've heard a few people say they believe they know who, in fact, their Guardian Angel might be. I cannot explain to you exactly how this happens to me, but I refer to my spirit guide as a "voice within," and it has spoken to me many times. Many months after the lack of response from both the hospital and the magazine had long ceased to enter my thoughts and was a closed issue as far as I was concerned, my "voice within" spoke to me. The message was so clear, and the thought so positive that it was in reference to the unresponsiveness of both parties, that it could not possibly be misunderstood. It was an old Hopi saying:

"No answer is also an answer."

One rather disheartening experience involved a friend, Colleen, who had told me she suffered from asthma. Once I became aware of this, I decided that upon my next visit to the Clinic I would inquire about the herbal prescription that had been recommended for Stanley's wife (whom I'd met on my first visit to the Clinic), thinking it might also help Colleen. Marta made an appointment with Dr. Gutierrez just to discuss Colleen's asthma and ask if she could get the same prescription for her. He said he would be glad to write out the prescription for Colleen, and asked if we had an herbal pharmacy near us in Massachusetts. Since Marta did not know of one, Dr. Gutierrez included the telephone number and address of a place in Dallas where the herbal prescription could be filled if we couldn't find a pharmacy closer to home.

Upon returning home I called the pharmacy in Dallas, and then sent them the prescription Dr. Gutierrez had written out, with enough money to cover the cost. In return, the asthma capsules were mailed to me. When I next saw Colleen, I gave her the capsules and told her she would have to take them for several weeks and possibly as long as six months before they could make a difference. I explained to her how much they had helped Stanley's wife and hoped they would be equally beneficial for her. When I saw her a couple of weeks later, I asked her how she was doing with the prescription. She told me that she had thrown it all away, never taking any of it, because her daughter (a nurse) warned her about the great risks associated with taking anything herbal. Her daughter said it could be quite dangerous—she was sure at least one of the herbs listed could be poisonous. How could Colleen think that I would give her something that could possibly hurt her? How could her daughter suggest such a thing? I forced myself not to take it personally, because I knew the real reason behind it was the prevalent attitude of the medical profession, of which her daughter is a part. I'm sure Colleen's daughter felt she was protecting her mother, but I believe in reality she may have prevented her mother from enjoying at least some, if not complete, relief from her asthma.

As I look back on the numerous appointments I had with various doctors, I realize that one meeting with Dr. West made the greatest impression on me. At this particular appointment, he told me that Dr. Simms (one of the primary care doctors who was not interested in having me as a patient) now had cancer herself. I remember saying something to the effect that she had not been the least bit interested in what I was doing for treatment, but that maybe it could help her. He went on to say that she was not doing at all well, and in thinking of my reply afterwards I felt that it must have sounded rather cold, but I did not mean it that way. However, I am sure she did everything modern medicine suggests, and I truly hoped she was not suffering as so many do. I never heard anything more about Dr. Simms, but judging by my conversation with Dr. West, her chances for recovery did not look promising.

After repeated visits to Dr. West, he would jokingly ask me why I came, and I would say I was "just keeping my promise." It was very comforting to have established such a good rapport with him. After the seventh year, however, he said that it was quite apparent that all was well with me, and he did not feel any further visits were necessary. Then, he added rather jokingly that I could send him a postcard now and then so he'd know what I was up to. At this time he said a very unusual and surprising thing. He asked me how often I came to Massachusetts. "I live here," I replied, totally taken aback by his assumption that I was just visiting. It was suddenly obvious to me that he was of the opinion that I spent a great deal of time in California, presumably much of it at the Clinic. I realized then that he was only familiar with the media's presentation of prolonged stays at expensive alternative clinics. I explained that I did go to San Diego every summer, usually staying a week, but while I was there I spent just one day at the Clinic (a fact I know I had mentioned to him more than once). I had never spent any significant amount of time at the Clinic—even my first visit was only for a day. Apparently he never fully grasped the fact that most patients only visit the Clinic for one day each time they go. Perhaps he felt I must be holding something back, as the entire treatment seemed too simple to be effective.

During my visits to the Clinic, I frequently heard about patients who had come because a friend had told them of the place. It was my own greatest desire to present information about the Bio-Medical Center to someone, to have them go there as I did, and to become well. However, one of my first experiences sharing information about the Clinic with another person can only be described as frustrating. I gave the information to an acquaintance in the hopes that it would be relayed to their relative who had been diagnosed with cancer. Later, I heard that the information was not conveyed because others had convinced him that I had simply been misdiagnosed, and to pass along false information and hope would be wrong. There was nothing I could think of that could undo this unfortunate turn of events. The person I had given the information to now totally dismissed it and I had no idea who the relative was, so I couldn't talk to her firsthand. Words cannot describe the feeling—the helplessness and frustration—knowing that she might have been helped by the Clinic but never had the opportunity to decide for herself.

While I sometimes reflect on the possibility that my surgery might not have been necessary, I am now grateful that it was done. My cancer is on a slide at the hospital. No one can say I was misdiagnosed and that the Clinic did nothing, but simply took my money. Without this confirmation, in many people's minds my words would mean little. Unfortunately I do not always have the opportunity to make this fact known.

Chapter 2

Attempts to Heal

One evening Marta called to tell me she had just spoken to her friend Mark, who works at the San Diego hotel used by some of the patients from the Clinic. Mark had given my phone number to a lady who said she had spent a week in Tijuana accompanied by a doctor from the Clinic. Mark told the woman I had been to the Clinic several times, and that he also knew many other people who were patients there. The lady said she was impressed with the Clinic and with the doctor who had shown her around, noting that he had pointed out various alternative treatment facilities in the area. The woman also said that the doctor had agreed to be interviewed on a local TV program in her home state of New Jersey. This appearance was in connection with her company, which dealt with alternative healing using primarily herbs and vitamins.

The lady's name was Trudy, and she did call me a few days later. She expressed the fact that she was indeed impressed with the Clinic, and told me about a girl named Ruth who would be going there shortly. Apparently, the doctor Trudy had spent the week with had told her he was sure he could help Ruth. Trudy asked if Ruth might call me, as she felt it would be comforting for her to talk to someone who had been there. I assured her I would be glad to talk to Ruth.

A day or so later Ruth called. She told me that she was leaving for the Clinic in about a week, and asked me how long I had stayed. I explained that although I had been to the Clinic several times I had never stayed longer than a single day—one day each year. She said she expected to stay longer. Not knowing Ruth's circumstances, but aware that some patients do require several days at the Clinic, I told her this was sometimes necessary but might not be in her case. She seemed to think that a one-day stay was unusual, but was content with waiting to find out how long she'd stay after she got there. I asked if she needed information regarding transportation over the border, explaining that Marta and I traveled with Dennis and I would be glad to give her his number. She replied that she was being picked up at the airport, and she would ask if the driver's name was Dennis. At this point she thanked me and the conversation ended.

As I hung up the phone, I suddenly had the awful feeling that something was just not right—I had the distinct panicky feeling that we were quite possibly talking about two different places. At that moment, I realized that never in a conversation with either Trudy or Ruth had the full name of the Bio-Medical Center been used—we had only referred to "the Clinic." At that moment I just knew Dennis would not be picking Ruth up at the airport, and no one else from the Bio-Medical Center would be, either. Feasibly, the only place which would supply this type of service would be a costly alternative spa-like clinic, and such a place would certainly have a patient stay for a prolonged length of time. I reasoned this had to be why my one-day stay seemed so strange to her.

My thoughts then flew to my conversation with Trudy. I thought about what she'd told me: A doctor was willing to travel to New Jersey to do a TV show, and he had escorted her around Tijuana for a full week. The Clinic had never been into advertising, and I simply could not imagine any of the doctors spending such a significant amount of time away from their patients. It all seemed so impossible. Why did I not sense these inconsistencies from the beginning? But even Mark assumed it was the Bio-Medical Center when he had talked to her. How I wished I had asked Trudy more questions! I could not help but wonder if she had been taken in by the "doctor"—was she too trustful and unquestioning—just as I had been during this entire turn of events. Surely Trudy, in charge of a company primarily interested in helping people, would not recommend clients go to an alternative clinic unless she was convinced the place was not only on the up-and-up but that the client would benefit from the experience. Trudy had said the doctor felt he could help Ruth. I prayed that wherever Ruth ended up the outcome for her would be nothing but good. My regrets were many over this incident. I vowed that in the future I would not make the mistake again of assuming so much, and I would ask many questions.

Some time later, I received a very large and complete book containing information on virtually every ailment known to man, each section of the book containing a list of the various vitamins and supplements beneficial for each ailment. It was from Trudy. Included with the book was an order form from her company, through which all the recommended vitamins and supplements could be purchased.

The book was no doubt costly, and I wondered if she thought of me as an obvious new client. However, since I would not be placing an order, I decided that a "thank you" of some sort was in order. It just so happened that I had obtained copies of a new video about the Bio-Medical Center, so I decided to send one to her. A man and woman from Alaska, both former Bio-Medical Center patients, created and distributed this video when they noticed the old one was made approximately 15 years ago and was in need of updating. They were a married couple with a family and they produced the video out of gratitude and commitment to the Clinic; they claimed their children would be orphans had they not been able to take advantage of the Hoxsey therapy.

At this point, I felt strongly that the clinic Trudy was promoting in Tijuana was not the Bio-Medical Center, and I also felt that the "doctor" had probably not included the Bio-Medical Center on his tour of alternative treatment facilities. Because of my suspicions, when I mailed Trudy the video I included a thank you note for the book which said, "Just in case this place was not on your tour, I hope that when you next visit Tijuana you make it a point to get there." I never heard from her again.

Ruth's desire to find an alternative approach to her cancer was not unlike the quest of a man named Stephen whom my daughter Marta met a few years ago, not long after our first couple of visits to the Bio-Medical Center. Stephen, she discovered, had been trying for years to locate an herbal center in Mexico he'd heard about, but the name and location were unknown to him—he believed it was located in Tijuana, but he was not sure. He told Marta he had a book listing many alternative clinics in Mexico, but if the place he was looking for was included in the book he was unable to identify it.

Marta told him all about me and our visits to the Bio-Medical Center, and said she thought it might be the place he had in mind. After hearing a little about the Clinic he was sure this was the place he had heard of long ago. Stephen was very thin, and it was apparent that he had lost a considerable amount of weight. He told Marta there were many days he did not feel well. However, he also went on to tell her that he had, on his own, researched and was using various alternative approaches to treating cancer. He explained that he altered his lifestyle, eating nourishing meals, choosing fresh and unprocessed foods, and taking vitamins he felt would be beneficial. Although he'd had cancer for several years, his doctor told him that his healthy lifestyle had already lengthened his life, possibly by as much as five years.

Marta gave him the information about the Clinic, and it was not long before he was there. Stephen lived in New Hampshire, and upon returning from his first visit to the Clinic he called Marta to thank her and to tell her that he felt better than he had in a long time. It is possible that Stephen's advanced cancer required additional time and visits to the Clinic, but he never talked about the details. He had a very positive attitude, and only stressed his improvements, even though he realized his time was limited.

Although Marta did hear from him again on a couple of other occasions and he was always upbeat, Stephen's sense was right. It was late for him. While the tonic and treatment helped him and definitely made him feel better, he died some months later. Without a doubt, the quality of his life during these last few months was considerably better than it might otherwise have been had he not visited the Clinic at all. To quote Mildred Nelson from an interview she gave for "Whole Life Times" in 1984: "When we lose one, we don't lose 'em in the condition like they do across the border—wasting away in pain."[1]   For this the Clinic patients who do die, as well as their loved ones, are grateful.

Many people travel great distances seeking alternative treatment at the Bio-Medical Center, having heard about it from friends and relatives. This fact is well known at the Clinic, where international travelers are not uncommon. There are people, however, who, when confronted with cancer, would prefer another avenue rather than the all too well known conventional treatments, but unfortunately are not familiar with alternative procedures and know of no one who has traveled this unfamiliar path. Perhaps these people have been acquainted with the suffering of a loved one or a close friend and these memories trigger a fear and hopelessness.

Recently, a book has been written by Michael Gearin-Tosh, a 54 year old teacher at Oxford University in England who was confronted with this situation, and has written about his experiences. Michael Gearin-Tosh was diagnosed with multiple myeloma (bone cancer). His doctor informed him there was no cure, but chemo was to be started immediately. Wondering why he was to have four months of chemo when there "was no cure," Gearin-Tosh decided to take matters into his own hands. He refused all traditional treatment and (just as Stephen had done waiting for the Clinic) resorted to his own devices, researching medical books and looking into alternative recommendations. He combined various alternative procedures and came up with his own independent treatment plan. I found his conversations with doctors with regard to his decision enlightening and surprising, and I'm sure anyone else reading the book will agree. Interestingly, eight years later, Gearin-Tosh has lived much longer than the one- to four-year survival time common for patients who undergo traditional treatment for this type of cancer.

The search for alternative means of healing is a process that is becoming more and more prevalent as individuals realize the all-too-numerous shortcomings of chemo and radiation, or when they hope to avoid the very unpleasant, dreaded side effects. My trips to the Bio-Medical Center have shown me that recovery is possible, and that being very much alive after many years is not exceptionally unusual. I have talked to many people who experienced the shrinking of tumors after taking the Hoxsey tonic and following the prescribed diet, and I realize that harsh treatment is not a must. I now also firmly believe that nutrition plays an important part not only in helping oneself towards wellness, but in preventing illness as well.

When I think of Eva, well for so many years, I will be forever grateful that my friend Bonny told me about her. Unlike Eva, however, Bonny's friend Fred chose to have his cancer treated conventionally when he was diagnosed. Fred and his wife rejected all they had heard about Eva and the Clinic (even though they knew Eva personally), and during the ensuing months followed all of the methods prescribed by his doctors. Bonny told me how Fred steadily lost weight, becoming sicker each week, until finally his doctors told him they had done everything that could possibly be done for him. At this point, according to Bonny, he wanted to call the Clinic after all, but he was now very sick and unable to travel. The call was never made. He died a very short time afterwards. I did not know Fred; I only heard about him through our mutual friend Bonny, who was deeply moved by his illness and passing. There is no way to know if things might have turned out differently had he gone to the Clinic, but Bonny and I both felt that he would not have suffered so much if he'd been a patient there.

No matter how many stories one hears—good or bad—nothing affects us more than when illness strikes a friend. When we hear good news, we experience gladness, and bad news brings sorrow. But the hopelessness that descends when a friend becomes seriously ill is lingering, and the emptiness we feel when someone is lost remains with us indefinitely. We not only feel a personal loss, but also realize the loss for the family, knowing that each anniversary or holiday will again remind them of someone special who is no longer there.

Such is the case with Susan. She was someone I did not have the privilege to know for a long time and our visits were infrequent, as she lived a considerable distance from me. But I looked forward to our short visits, always enjoying her company.

It came as a shock to hear she had been diagnosed with cancer, had surgery, and was going through the conventional follow-up treatments.

Shortly after I heard the news, her husband Ralph called me. He felt that the addition of the Hoxsey tonic might be good for her, knowing I had taken it with positive results. He said her doctor approved of any alternative procedures Susan might consider, and I told him he was lucky she had found such a doctor—this was not often the case. I gave Ralph the phone number of the Clinic, and shortly thereafter Ralph's son flew down and talked to one of the doctors regarding his mother. He returned with the tonic and instructions about the diet Susan was to follow.

Some time later I heard Susan was feeling better—getting out with friends again and planning to visit the Clinic herself in two weeks. This news was promising; it seemed she was on the right path. Before the trip took place, however, a visit to her doctor changed her plans. Her doctor now stated that she only had six months left unless aggressive procedures were followed immediately.

What could be more devastating than hearing such a prognosis? Unless you or a loved one have been in this position, it is impossible to understand the trauma. When confronted with news of this magnitude, there is no time to think things over, and the only alternative that seems to make sense is to follow the doctor's advice. To go against these recommendations can make you feel as though your loved one would be deprived of their last opportunity to get well. The aggressive procedure was started, leaving Susan too sick to make the trip to Mexico. She became weaker, and perhaps just gave up.

There is no way of knowing if things could have ended differently had the trip been made. Whatever path a person chooses, there are no guarantees. We may wonder about many things, but we can find comfort, at least, in knowing the suffering has ended. I know Susan will always be with us in spirit.

Chapter 3

It Takes the Fear Out

In the years that I have returned to California and the Clinic for my annual checkup, I have seen many changes. The San Diego airport is now much larger. The building appears twice the original size due to an addition that is largely glass, bringing the feeling of the city indoors. A new passageway, also glass, leads to and overlooks the baggage area, located at ground level, and small palm trees line this second level passageway, offering a prelude to what is to come once you step outside.

Due to the popularity of San Diego as an ideal vacation spot, the number of passengers has increased. However, the well-designed layout of the terminal ensures smooth traffic flow and surprisingly little congestion. As we step outside we are greeted by the familiar flowers and palm trees, and are joined by dozens of tourists lining the walk waiting for car rentals or hotel vans.

Now when Marta and I return, we stay at a hotel with an ocean view and remain in the city for a full week, having met caring people who helped us find wonderful accommodations. Each time I arrive at this lovely hotel, thinking of my upcoming checkup (usually the following day) I am overwhelmed by my good fortune and especially my good health, for it all could have been so different. Indeed, as the years have passed the trip has become more of a vacation than anything else! We have visited almost every tourist attraction in the immediate area, as well as many miles to the north and east. In fact, so many people back home are aware of our yearly jaunts that they frequently seek Marta out for suggestions when they are planning a trip to the San Diego area.

The Clinic, too, has seen some changes since my first visit. Mildred Nelson passed away in 1999, leaving her sister Liz Jonas in charge of her wonderful legacy. Two doctors who were there when I first arrived have left—one to pursue a private practice, one to become more involved in special surgical procedures—but equally fine and dedicated physicians have replaced them. Dennis still works for the Clinic, transporting people from San Diego to Tijuana daily. Leona has passed away, leaving this service solely in his hands. Perhaps because he feels it a little "unmanly," he has removed the "TLC" from the sides of his station wagon, but the meaning remains nonetheless. As before, Dennis also introduces new patients to the procedures, giving them a little history of the Clinic, and generally making them feel welcome. And, as before, van service is provided daily from San Ysidro (located midway between San Diego and the border) to the Clinic. The building itself has remained unchanged except for cosmetic touches, possibly Liz's influence. Some of the dark woodwork has been painted the same pale blue color as the walls, giving an open, flowing feeling to the interior. The large wooden desk for returning patients has been replaced by a modern, sleek, pale blue desk, and to complete this picture the green robes that were once so familiar have been replaced by (you guessed it) blue ones. The walkway from the Clinic to the x-ray building is now enclosed in glass. Flowers line the inside of this walkway, and the swimming pool that was once almost obscured is now surrounded by carefully attended flowerbeds. The pool itself, however, remains empty and unused. The café remains unchanged, the open moneybox still stands at the doorway, and your meal is prepared before you. And, last but by no means least, the friendly, caring atmosphere remains, ensuring that patients feel welcome, respected and reassured.

As always, patients and their loved ones appreciate the Bio-Medical's continuing openness to research, and the fact that they are up-to-date on all that is taking place in hospitals in the States. If a new procedure looks promising, and if the doctors feel it may help a patient, they do not hesitate to incorporate it into their treatment. While all facts regarding a person's diagnosis are explained fully and truthfully, and nothing is withheld, the Clinic's medical staff is willing to consider a patient's preferences if at all possible.

Unfortunately, the approach of today's medical profession is all too often geared towards efficiency, and explaining everything to a patient is apparently considered too time-consuming. Time saving procedures may work well in some institutions, but they do not belong in a doctor's office. Blind efficiency frequently leaves the patient feeling rushed, empty and uncared for.

On the flip–side, an overly–efficient approach can also leave the doctor unsatisfied. In a discussion with Dr. Trujillo, my attending physician at my latest check–up at the Clinic, expressed this feeling when he spoke of his experiences in conventional hospitals. He said the time limits made it almost impossible to get to know a patient on an individual basis, and all too often the conventional treatment was not successful, compounding the frustration. In contrast, he stated, the Bio-Medical Center allows time for explanations, and offers doctors the extremely rewarding experience of actually watching a patient get better.

When I explained to Dr. Trujillo that I was writing this book, he was very helpful in explaining to me when and how chemo is used at the Clinic. He explained that new patients are always started immediately on the Hoxsey tonic. Only if a patient does not respond, or in extremely serious, life-threatening cases where it is evident the patient has come in the very late stages of cancer is chemo used—and then sparingly. In these cases chemo is administered once a week at the lowest doses possible, while the patient continues on the Hoxsey tonic and diet. Dr. Trujillo further explained that the addition of the tonic at this time helps to eliminate the loss of hair and the sickness that usual accompanies chemo. The chemo treatment is repeated only as often as absolutely necessary. Dr. Trujillo made it clear that chemo is not given as a cure and is done only to grant the time necessary for the tonic to begin to work alone (it takes three months for the tonic to detoxify the body). He also stated that the Clinic does not believe in using radiation at all.

Each year, with every visit to the Clinic, Marta and I continue to meet interesting people. We have met people from all walks of life and from many diverse areas and countries. The Bio-Medical Center has remained a comfortable and inviting environment where patients continue to converse together, sharing experiences and encouragement. Sometimes recipes are exchanged, which are especially welcomed by new patients who must suddenly avoid certain foods and who often find the dietary restrictions overwhelming.

Many people coming to the Clinic were introduced to it by a friend who had either been there themselves or knew someone who had come. This is a comfort when visiting for the first time. New patients are facing not only an unknown, but also the fact that they have cancer. Questions loom: Is this the answer? Should they listen to their doctors back home? Could this treatment really help them? After arriving, however, there is little doubt that most feel they have made the right decision.

The countless moments Marta and I spent with everyone there remain with me as special. The openness of these conversations allow for a gratifying closeness, even though our time is brief. Back home, conversations like this may never be achieved, even with unlimited time.

Among the people we met on later visits was an elderly man who had been told by his hometown doctor to "go home and put his affairs in order." He told us that he came to the Clinic instead and was told to "go home and get well." He explained that his first visit was eighteen months ago and he was now doing fine. He had been given his new supply of tonic just before we talked to him, and he planned to return for a checkup in another three months.

Also, on a later trip, we met a lady who told us her first visit to the Clinic was when it was located in Dallas 50 years ago. She had been well these many years but now, after all this time, she had again been diagnosed with cancer and was once more returning to the Clinic. She did not tell us what kind of cancer it was, but it may have been a skin cancer because her treatment involved applications of some type and she would be returning for additional treatments. As she was leaving, her parting words to me were: "This is the only place to go"—to which I could only reply: "You are not telling me anything I don't already know."

One day, I spent time talking with a couple from the state of New Mexico, who informed me that several people from their home town had been, or are, patients at the Clinic. Because of this, the husband had been able to procure enough tonic from a neighbor to carry him through until his own Clinic visit. Later on the same day, I met a woman from Tennessee. She and her husband had traveled to the Clinic with another woman from their home state. They were all so friendly together that I had assumed they were old friends. Instead, I discovered they had just met as they were leaving for the Clinic a few days before. However their friendship began, I doubt it ended when they returned home.

Perhaps the most heartbreaking case I can recall involved a lady who had recently married (perhaps for the second time, as she was middle-aged), only to find out a short time later that she had a tumor, which had to be removed. From what she said the tumor was not especially large, but her doctor advised against a lumpectomy because it would be "too disfiguring," in his words. Apparently he did not specify what the alternative would be.

She woke up with her entire breast removed, and it was clear that she was still in a state of disbelief over what had happened to her. This was the last thing she had wanted, and she could not believe that her doctor could possibly think this was the "better" solution. She was totally shaken but knew that she wanted no part of the follow-up procedures (quite possibly involving the removal of lymph nodes), so she came to the Clinic on the recommendation of a friend. It was clear that her husband, who had accompanied her, was doing all he could to help and comfort her, but on that day she appeared to be beyond consoling.

Time did not always allow us to hear the complete stories or backgrounds of the people we met at the Clinic, but I can assure you there must be hundreds of stories—in some ways quite similar yet as different as night and day. We met several people from Australia, not any that came by busload as Dennis had once described, but who came alone or accompanied by a friend or relative. One lovely grandmother I remember especially well said she only came to the Clinic every other year because the trip from Australia was so long. She never did say what kind of cancer she had—or possibly used to have—but she seemed quite well as she showed us pictures of her grandchildren, saying she'd return in another two years.

Twice while we were at the Clinic patients told us that the doctor there told them to return home, because in their cases surgery was necessary and must be done first. After the surgery they were to return to the Clinic and begin the Hoxsey treatment. I wondered how long it would take before doctors in this country would reciprocate by refering a patient to a place like the Bio-Medical Center, knowing it was in the patient's best interest not to perform surgery or suggest caustic treatment.

Once, while traveling back to San Diego, I mentioned to Dennis, who always supplied our transportation to and from the Clinic, how incredible it was that I was able hear so many different stories, considering that I'm only at the Clinic for one day each year. Of course Marta traveled with me, and she had the better part of the day to visit with other patients, never missing an opportunity to engage a person in conversation. This increased the number of people I met as well, for she always made certain I was introduced to everyone she met. Dennis had gotten to know Marta to some extent, so he smiled knowingly. "Just imagine," he said, "how many hundreds of stories she'd hear if she were here every day as I am." "Sometimes," he added, "I think I've heard them all and then along comes someone with yet another story."

Well perhaps Dennis has heard stranger, but of all the stories I heard, the most unbelievable was related by a man from Colorado. He told us he knew of a doctor who had come to the Clinic for treatment for himself, but upon returning home continued to treat his patients conventionally. I found this inconceivable. How could he subject his patients to something he himself did not want to face? Did he also prevent his patients from receiving the benefits he enjoyed at the Clinic? I've heard the observation that "truth is stranger than fiction"—this has to be a classic example of that truism.

It is possible to talk to the other patients at the Clinic in ways that I find impossible back home, and in some cases the terminology used differs as well. For instance, I do not believe I ever heard anyone at the Clinic use the word "survivor." However, this is often how a person who has had cancer might be described back home—sometimes by acquaintances and sometimes even by the patient himself.

Growing up, I remember "survivor" referring to people who had escaped epic tragedies like fire, war, landslides, etc. The word was not applied to disease. No one was a "flu survivor," and not even a person who lived through an extremely severe heart attack ever referred to himself as a "heart attack survivor." But now the term is used with regard to cancer, the only possible reason being that the disease has reached epidemic proportions, leaving few families untouched. The word "cancer" brings fear to the hearts of the general public. Newspapers and magazines are full of stories of these "survivors." Hardly a week goes by that we don't read a heartbreaking story of a small sick child, mothers and daughters battling the disease together, or even favorite actors or athletes being affected. We read about the loss of hair, the weakness and the nausea caused by chemo or radiation, and the trauma which wracks the entire family. There are stories of support groups of all kinds, not to mention various "survivor" groups, and no one thinks of the latter as survivors of anything other than cancer.

Early detection is proclaimed to be in everyone's best interest, as the media constantly reminds us to get our checkups, mammograms, etc., but this does not seem to stem the rapidly advancing cancer disaster. The truth is that the epidemic seems to be getting worse, not better. Early detection leads to some "survivors," but all too often—early detection or not—the result is early death.

When I voice the fact that little advance or change has been made in the field of cancer treatment in the last fifty years here in the States, people remind me that millions are now being spent on cancer research and the cure seems to be just around the corner. They believe that "by next year" (or maybe shortly after that) there will be a cure. It seems I have heard this said for quite a few years now. In fact, this mindset is so prevalent and we are reminded of it so constantly that it nearly affected my decision to write this book. I thought it quite possible that the project would be irrelevant before it's completion because cancer would cease to exist. The January 1996 issue of a nutrition publication I happened to pick up at a market contained a short article on breast cancer which stated, "We're a few decades late in getting started…but we'll know a lot more in the next 5 years." Well, those 5 years have come and gone, and while there have been a few advances made I do not feel "a lot more" has been learned.

Since I have been going to the Clinic I have lost friends, or heard about the friends and family of others who did not actually die from cancer but who simply did not survive the extreme effects of chemotherapy. True, the cause of death is listed on the death certificate as a heart attack or some other medical problem, but the cardiac arrest (or whatever) was, without a doubt, caused or hastened by the attempt to cure the cancer. I have heard a few people voice the opinion that medical procedures somehow contributed to the loss of a loved one, but many more people do not like to face this possibility and are not likely to express it. "The doctor is not at fault—he did everything in his power." What could more accurately be said in some of these cases is that the doctor did too much. He did not give the person a chance to build up their resistance and strength, but immediately recommended what turned out to be too-harsh or too-frequent treatments. It is known that for every cancer cell chemo kills, it can kill up to ninety good ones. The body tries to replace these good cells but if the treatment continues regularly, if the doses given are strong and the patient is weak, it can be a losing battle.

When I was young, from time to time I heard of an elderly person (in their 70's, 80's or even 90's) finding out that they had cancer. It seemed to me at that time, almost without exception, a disease of the elderly. In many cases, it seems conceivable they had lived with the cancer for a long period of time, not even realizing they had it. It makes one wonder if they still would have lived these long, productive lives had the cancer been detected earlier, and they'd managed to live through the trauma of surgery and the follow-up treatment associated with it.

Today, people in the States find it difficult to believe there could be dedicated and knowledgeable medical doctors and nurses residing in Mexico. They find it even harder to believe that a nurse (although this title is inadequate) from Texas would not only accept the enormous responsibility of running a clinic but also move that clinic to Mexico in order to practice a more kindly and successful—not caustic—way to treat cancer. Financial gain, which is the reason most people make such moves, was definitely not the reason behind Mildred Nelson's decision to move the Bio-Medical Center out of the United States. Perhaps it is time for members of the medical profession in the United States to stop, stand back, and take a long, thoughtful look at a different approach. The treatment prescribed at the Bio-Medical Center is far from new. People have endorsed the Hoxsey treatment for over seventy years, not only in Texas but in seventeen other Clinics in the states. Ironically, people from many countries travel to Mexico to seek treatment at the Bio-Medical Center. It makes one wonder if people in other corners of the world are more open-minded.

Although most people realize the Bio-Medical Center treats cancer, many do not realize the Clinic also successfully treats many other ailments. Along with all types of malignancies, they also treat patients for circulatory ailments, diabetes, high cholesterol, kidney failure, and emphysema, to list just a few. There are several doctors on the well-qualified medical staff, which includes an oncologist, and Dr. Gutierrez, who is not only a medical doctor but also a certified herbalist.

Dr. Gutierrez's knowledge as an exceptionally fine physician was very apparent to my good friend Erik Magnusson, who visited the Clinic for the first time simply for a checkup. Erik was born in Sweden and explained the following to me:

"A tuberculosis vaccine was developed in the 1920's, Bacille Calmette-Guerin. Live but weakened tuberculosis bacteria were used for injections, providing some (but not complete) protection against the disease. All children born in Sweden in the 1940s through 1970 were inoculated. The vaccine produces antibodies which show up in some blood tests and are frequently mistaken for the presence of the disease itself. Over the years, physicians in the States have wanted to put me on INH, not understanding that I do not have TB. I have been urged to take medication for this non-existent disease on several occasions. Not so at the Clinic. For the first time in my life, a physician (Dr. Gutierrez) immediately recognized what was going on."

To say Erik was impressed is putting it mildly. He said Dr. Gutierrez immediately mentioned it to him, stating that while it showed up on the test, he realized it was from the inoculation Erik had been given as a child.

Many times I have thought about my good fortune in hearing about Eva through my friend Bonny. Somehow, God provided me with this opportunity and knowledge, and then gave me the courage to seek out what was at that time a "place of mystery."

Eight years ago when I was first diagnosed, the doctors in the States told me their success rate was about 75% (or, as I clearly remember one doctor phrasing it: "25% don't make it statistically"). The Bio-Medical Center's rate is 80%—quite impressive considering the number of people who begin the Clinic's regime during the later stages of their illness. When one also takes into account the fact that early detection is common in the U.S., the Clinic's higher percentage speaks for itself. This, along with many other reasons, reinforce the statement I heard when I arrived at the Bio-Medical Center for the first time: "It takes the fear out."

Part 3

Against the Silences

Chapter 1

To Save the Horses

It came as a great shock to me, although it surely was known to hundreds of other people. Yet I felt it was generally a secret well kept from the general public.

One day at work, Anjie handed me a magazine. Anjie is the Animal Control Officer for our town, who shares an office with me at the Police Department. It was a well-known animal rights magazine, which included an article about Robert Redford, Sylvester Stallone and Richard Gere joining the fight to end the suffering of horses used in the manufacture of estrogen-enhancing drugs. The article not only detailed the brutality to the horses but also noted the link between these drugs and cancer.

As I read the article, I learned for the first time that pregnant mares' urine is the major ingredient in the estrogen-enhancing drug, which had been prescribed for me many years before. All I could think of as I read this fact was: "Who and why and for what unfathomable reason would anyone decide to take a pregnant mare's urine into a laboratory to see if they could come up with some use for it in the first place?." The collection of the urine is all that matters on the dozens of farms that sell this "product." The lives of these mares is miserable—constantly pregnant and tethered for urine collection—only to eventually end up at the slaughterhouse.

Of course, in addition to mistreatment of the mares, another tragedy is the fate of their numerous offspring. The article explains that Redford, Stallone and Gere are attempting to aid in saving these foals—they each adopted one. The foals, most just babies and newly separated from their mothers, are kept in holding pens waiting to be auctioned off. The foals are packed thirty to a pen and sold in these lots of thirty. The scenario presented by the article is frighteningly brutal. The foals are wobbly on their legs and frightened. If one is too sick to stand up it is dragged to its feet, since a sickly colt isn't marketable. The people who buy these animals are mostly from "feed lots," where colts are fattened and slaughtered. Although some are saved—adopted by caring individuals—hundreds more are not so lucky.

Since 1998, when this article appeared in the animal rights magazine, I have noticed a couple of other articles in women's magazines regarding estrogen-enhancing drugs. One such article used the caption "Smell the pee," beneath a photo of a capsule broken in half. Although unpleasant, at least this type of media attention is an indication that the truth about this prescription medicine is becoming known.

Four years after this article appeared in the animal rights magazine, a hormone replacement therapy study was conducted, showing that questions had finally been raised about the use of estrogen-enhancing drugs, especially for prolonged periods of time. Articles confirming this appeared in various publications, stating that "researchers recognize several shortcomings" with the therapy, also noting that while there are "benefits," there are also "greater risks than previously thought," clearly showing that the benefits have been overemphasized. The articles also state that while many pharmaceutical companies advertise that their products protect against osteoporosis and heart disease, each of the drugs has it's own side effects. This study has resulted in many women deciding to discontinue this type of therapy. This reduction in the sale of estrogen-enhancing drugs will hopefully be the beginning of the end of demand for this "product." As the 1998 article suggests: "You can help" by making a switch to more humane hormone products (if you are still taking one at all). If you are uncertain about a product you may now be using, I urge you to check the web, which offers a great deal of information.

If wishes and hopes could come true, I would end the nightmare for the horses today, but as long as there is a demand for the product this will not be. Perhaps word of mouth, along with articles in women's magazines, information passed along in animal publications, and the fact that newspapers are warning the public, it will finally come to a halt. Hopefully in the not-too-distant future, these unfortunate foals will no longer be available but unfortunately even as I write this, the brutality continues.

Chapter 2

Surgery as Prevention?

We live, unquestionably, in an age of science and technology. The rate at which new discoveries are made is dizzying. Projects and procedures deemed impossible less than a decade ago are now routine, improving our daily lives in both minor and dramatic ways.

In contrast, several years ago the American Medical Association suggested a method of breast cancer prevention that, in my opinion, can only be described as primitive. If there was a high risk of breast cancer in your family (i.e., if your mother, sister, aunt, etc. had been a victim), the suggested method of prevention was to have your breasts surgically removed.

How could the AMA suggest something that seemed nothing short of barbaric? The public apparently took it in stride, as I do not remember ever hearing anyone questioning the procedure after it was announced by the media. I thought there would be an outcry from women everywhere, but this was not the case. Was I the only one who thought this was positively ludicrous—that this was not an acceptable answer?

Eight years ago when I was first diagnosed, one of the doctors told me this was an option. He told me of a young woman who had, just a short time before, had both of her breasts removed as a precaution. And indeed, I did hear of other women who opted for this extreme solution in order to avoid the possibility of breast cancer, and many of them were surprisingly young.

In 2002, the medical community once again proposed another similar "solution." In May of that year, on the front page of our daily newspaper, the removal of ovaries was suggested. The headline read, "Removal of Ovaries Can Cut Cancer Risk," and the article states that removing ovaries was shown to significantly reduce the risk not only of ovarian cancer, but also of breast cancer. It mentioned two studies published by the New England Journal of Medicine on its website and presented at the American Society of Clinical Oncology's annual meeting. Since then, I have noticed other reminders regarding the removal of ovaries as a precautionary option, especially in cases where women had developed breast cancer.

I realize all too well that there are times and circumstances where drastic surgical procedures are necessary. However, is it necessary to promote these procedures as a means of prevention? I cannot help but feel that with such drastic suggestions, modern medicine is acknowledging a defeat. Certainly these radical surgeries could eliminate the potential for some cancers but it is not, and certainly should not be considered an acceptable or satisfactory final solution.

Instead, the answer has to be a cure, a wellness resulting from ridding the body of the disease, or preventative measures put in place before the disease can strike. These measures could include proper diet, vitamins and any other medical procedures which ensure health without destroying healthy cells.

Obviously, cancer cannot strike a breast that is no longer there, but prevention has to be more thoughtful than the removal of body parts. That surgery might be the foremost thought in any prevention program is more than a little alarming. Even the suggestion makes one wonder what might be suggested next. Hopefully, the next preventative measure suggested by the medical community will not include surgery.

Chapter 3

Nature's Gifts

Lately there has been a great deal of interest in the possibility that cancer cures may be found in the jungles of Central and South America. Twenty years ago most "men of science" would have laughed at the idea that perhaps something could be learned from the natives and Shamans living in these far away places. The fact that the natives practiced their own brand of doctoring, effectively curing many ailments and diseases, would have been discounted as exaggerated at best. However, lately we have realized that these people are extremely knowledgeable about medicinal plants and are often expert in treating many different diseases. In fact, the number of plants they routinely use number as high as 100 or more, and not infrequently a combination of two or more herbs may be used simultaneously when treating a given disorder or disease. Even in the study of a single plant, the more knowledge we acquire, the more our ignorance of the possibilities comes to light.

The current interest and research seems to primarily target plants from far away places as the solution for many ills, as well as the cure for countless others. But long before the time of the Pilgrims, the people living on our American shores recognized and used dozens and dozens of plants, not only to treat sores and wounds and to heal diseases, but also for birth control. Not only did Native Americans have healthful diets, but they practiced good hygiene, bathing frequently and practicing dental hygiene as well, chewing such herbs as sage or peppermint leaves, or fennel seeds. These herbs not only sweeten the breath but help to combat the bacteria which causes bad breath, working much better than many of the products on the market today which make such claims. To Native Americans, the outdoors fulfilled all of their needs—indeed it was a pharmacy at their fingertips. There is little doubt that before the arrival of the white man the natives enjoyed holistic health in it's finest form. The fine physiques of the natives were recorded over and over again by the first explorers reaching our shores—a true testament to a healthy lifestyle and diet. The medicinal plants that grew here before the white man arrived are in all likelihood still here. Unfortunately, because of the over harvesting of many indigenous plants, there are those that are now extinct or on an endangered species list. In addition, all too many places the Indians held as sacred—possibly because of the God-given plants growing there—have been threatened, and in some cases destroyed by civilization and by our ignorance of their value.

It has been suggested that primitive man learned of many healing plants by watching animals, who seem to instinctively know how to help themselves. For example, a deer chews aspen bark, which we now know contains elements that act in like manner as aspirin. It is also more than likely that primitive man had his own innate capability to recognize edible and medicinal plants—a capability all but lost with the advance of civilization. However, I recently spoke to a friend who has studied survival techniques under various difficult circumstances for several years, and his firsthand experiences strongly suggest that these capabilities and instincts can be regained or relearned if a person spends adequate time in this pursuit.

Today, however, there is very little that encourages us on a day-to-day basis to regain or learn this lost knowledge. Indeed we are, in fact, in many ways encouraged to distrust herbal remedies. Many of these warnings appear to originate from large pharmaceutical companies, where increased interest in herbal products might undermine profits. Very few individuals are aware of the edible and medicinal plants that their grandmothers kept handy to apply to cuts, insect bites and the like, not to mention what she might keep in her cupboard to add to teas or soups when one was ill. Today we simply make a trip to the nearest drug store for items necessary to alleviate any of these minor ills or complaints, where there is always someone willing to make money on our lack of knowledge.

The mission of the medical community and pharmaceutical industry in promoting prescription drugs, from all outward appearances, seems to be more than successful judging from ads shown daily on television. These drugs are advertised (even while listing numerous side effects that often sound as bad as the original ailment) promising all kinds of cures. It seems nothing is impossible if you are simply taking the right prescription.

I'm not suggesting that no one is in need of a doctor–prescribed drug at one time or another, and I know that for some people it is a daily necessity. I have noticed, however, through listening and observing, what appears to be, in many cases, drugs being prescribed too freely. However, as long as doctors are willing to write out prescriptions without first considering an alternative approach, the public sees it as the only way to go. No one is more aware of how many older citizens, or even younger members of the general public, are totally dependent on prescription drugs than the politicians. Part of almost any political speech is geared to assuring the voters that the cost of these drugs will remain within their reach. Until we start thinking about viable, non–addicting alternatives, the trend will only escalate.

Perhaps like the old chicken soup remedy we are all well acquainted with, the Hoxsey tonic also works. The herbal formula in the Hoxsey tonic has not changed since first introduced in the 1920's, reminding me of a philosophy often quoted by one of the officers I work with: "If it's not broke, don't fix it."

Recently, a reporter who has written about conventional and alternative medicine in print, broadcasting and film for over two decades noted that Linus Pauling—a pioneer of innovative medicine—made a statement shortly before he died in 1994 at age 93 in which he noted that the inspiration for modern medicine's turn towards more holistic options was coming from the bottom up—from the people—not from the top down. The same reporter has voiced the opinion that almost three decades of reporting in the field of complementary alternative medicine have reinforced his view that the Hoxsey Therapy is the most interesting and impressive of the modern alternative approaches to treating cancer. He is aware that the Hoxsey Therapy is the oldest alternative cancer treatment in continuous use, originating in mid-19th century America. He also realizes that this treatment (relying exclusively on word-of-mouth patient referrals) has treated scores of thousands of people with cancer, many of them at the very late stages, with apparent success.

Not long ago while only half paying attention to a program on television, I heard this statement: "We have entered into an explosion of knowledge regarding plants." The inference was misleading, suggesting that modern man is just now discovering the use of plants—that this was never done before. In fact, we are in actuality coming back to the earth—rediscovering what was once widely known and accepted. Yet many educated people today appear to be ignorant of what was accomplished and known in the past, and refer to it as "new."

Much of modern medicine is built upon lessons learned long ago. However, I have no doubt that someday soon a renowned doctor or scientist will announce a "medical breakthrough," having discovered (actually rediscovered) the unique healing possible when we tap the gifts of the earth. It will likely be something the Indians or the Shamans knew all along, because they realized the earth is a bountiful medicine place. But unfortunately, that fact will undoubtedly be lost in the excitement of the "discovery," with the doctor or scientist receiving acclaim for something "new."

In addition to the public's growing interest in alternative medicine, interest in organic foods has increased dramatically in the past few years. Not only have specialized health food stores become popular, but more and more local grocery stores are adding organic and health food sections. This increased interest in organic has also expanded to include baby products, cosmetics, and toiletry products.

It is encouraging to note that while the ads on our television sets continue to promote fast food items, quick meals and other time-saving but often less nourishing meals and snacks, people in increasing numbers are frequenting markets that specialize in fresh, wholesome foods. Most definitely, good health is of primary importance to many people, a trend I find most heartening in light of my own experiences.

My hope is that this ever-increasing interest in organic food will also give us a fuller realization of the wonders of nature. Gratefulness is all too often forgotten as the blessings of the bounties we enjoy are taken for granted. Let us not forget that every growing thing is a blessing from God.

Fortunately there are a few people today who are not only knowledgeable about plants and their many benefits but are also truly appreciative and thankful for them. My good friend Kathy, known to many as Eagle Mother, is such a person.

One late July day while visiting with Eagle Mother, she spoke of the wonders of the growing things on her property. Her raspberry bushes were full of berries and she told me how she would go out in the morning, bowl of cereal in hand, and as she picked each berry would say "thank you" as she placed it in her bowl.

As we go about our grocery shopping each week how many of us pause— even for a single moment—to think about where the raspberries in the box come from? Perhaps our seclusion from unspoiled land coupled with the sterile atmosphere of the supermarket, the packaging and the commercialism makes gratitude for all living things almost impossible.

Eagle Mother told me that when she is the passenger in a car, she looks along the sides of the roadways and can identify dozens of plants with multiple uses. This is incredible to me. I often look at the growing things along the roadways, and with the exception of being able to identify a few wild flowers there is nothing that to me would seem edible or usable. I'm afraid this is probably true for the majority of us.

Often a single plant has multiple uses, and there are many plants my friend can recognize and advise the use of. I asked if she would give me an example of a single common plant, along with it's description and a list of it's uses, for the benefit of my readers. She kindly consented to do this. She chose a plant which grows profusely on her property, known as "White Man's Foot;" the botanical name is Plantain. It is a plant most people only think of as a weed, and if found in their garden it would be destroyed. Eagle Mother gave me the following:

The Plantain

"Look out your back door and you're likely to find one of the most common plants in New England today. The Plantain is broad leafed, deeply veined, and grows from the roots at ground level. The leaves grow in a spiral fashion and at maturity spikes grow from the center and produce seeds along most of the length of the spike. Plantain is an abundant and hardy plant, growing in open fields, the sides of roads, disturbed lots, and in wet areas. Most folks encountering Plantain in their own backyards consider them to be a common lawn pest that needs to be eradicated. The Plantain would be welcome if more people knew of its medicinal and healing properties.

How many times in your yard have you been bitten by mosquitoes or May flies? Pick a few plantain leaves and crush them up or roll so the juice is extracted and rub this on your bite. The itch will be gone and the raised irritation will subside. You can even put a bandaid over the leaves as a poultice. It's also good for bee stings, rashes and poison ivy. You'll often find plaintain growing near or around poison ivy.

If you make a tea or infusion from the leaves it will be useful for diarrhea and irritations of the stomach. The tea can also help to relieve coughs and chronic lung afflictions such as asthma and bronchitis. It soothes the mucus membranes and promotes an expectorant action. A hemorrhoid salve can be prepared with the dried plant. The dried seeds are often used as a bulk laxative and some Native tribes added the seeds to the grains.

Consult a knowledgeable herbalist for the proper dosage and length of time for use. Knowledge and education of the herbal or "Green Kingdom" is healing and a great way to connect with our Mother Earth."

—Eagle Mother

It is obvious we would be far less destructive if we lived as Eagle Mother does. Not only might we find useful plants right outside our door, but our appreciation for these gifts would grow. Since we have become distant from and unfamiliar with wild plants, as beneficial as they may be, it would be foolish to attempt to use any before you have a thorough knowledge and understanding of each one. It is essential to make sure they are used safely. To use medicinal herbs indiscriminately would be as irresponsible as taking a prescription drug without the knowledge of what the medication is for. Eagle Mother has grown up using plants. This is how she lives.

If everyone could be fortunate enough to spend time with someone like Eagle Mother, I cannot help but believe we would discover anew how truly remarkable the earth is. If we would remember, every day, the wonders around us, surely in a very short time the destruction, carelessness, and often wanton unconcern for the woods, fields, and animals would cease.

Chapter 4

Food for Thought

My experiences at the Bio-Medical Center have more than proven to me the importance of good nutrition. Not only is it important to cancer patients while on the Hoxsey tonic, but it is of utmost importance to all of us at all times.

The past century has brought drastic changes in our environment. Pesticides, insecticides and air pollutants from cars and factories constantly affect the air we breathe, and our food is superimposed with preservatives, additives and food coloring. I am extremely aware of additives and preservatives in foods—reading labels has become second nature to me. Before I started on the Hoxsey tonic I'm sure I read labels the way many people tend to read them today. Fat content is checked, calories are noted, and perhaps vitamins are taken into account, but how often does the reader get to the most important part—the ingredients? On my first visit to the Bio-Medical Center, all of these things were brought to my attention. It is essentially impossible to avoid alien residues, as they are in virtually everything eaten, drunk or inhaled. But we can help ourselves by avoiding foods with long lists of additives and preservatives. We must begin by reading labels. This will help to arm us with the knowledge we need in order to avoid chemically modified and nutritionally inadequate foods, replacing them with fresh fruits, vegetables and whole grains. We can also help in the detoxification process by eating fruits and vegetables such as broccoli and blueberries, which are known to contain anti–oxidants. There are also a number of anti–oxidant products at health food stores.

There is also another factor to consider when purchasing packaged foods—advertising and commercialism on the label. It appears there are no hard and fast rules or laws governing the use of certain words on a food package. Should you be interested in purchasing a diet meal or low calorie product and the word "lite" is indicated, it does not necessarily mean low in caloric intake. It may simply mean "lite" in weight, and since many diet meals (as an example) are small portions, it may mean no more than this. I believe this is probably the most misused and misunderstood single word in product promotion. In fact, when purchasing any meal which you believe would be helpful when dieting, keep in mind that the wording on the label (or the first impression it encourages) could be misleading.

Only by reading the entire list of ingredients can you be sure of what has been added, or what is included in the food product you are purchasing. One of the examples I was given when I was first instructed to eliminate preservatives from my diet was bread. It was explained to me that bread is (or should be) a very simple food. Basically it is flour, yeast, milk, and shortening. However, when I read a label on a loaf of bread I was amazed to find a very lengthy list of ingredients on most loaves. Having been told not to buy any food item unless I was familiar with all of the ingredients listed, you can well imagine this eliminated many foods from my diet.

Color is also added to enhance the look of many products. It is very apparent in colored candy, and toppings on fancy cookies and cakes, all very appealing to children, but many people fail to notice that color is also found in cereals, jellies, and even in some packaged meals. I have no doubt that concerned parents constitute a large part of the growing interest in organic foods and the shifts to shopping in health food stores.

Preservatives are added to ensure a longer shelf life, but what happens when this same preservative which keeps the food from spoiling on the shelf enters your body? I cannot imagine that this same preservative, once eaten, just somehow disappears and becomes non–existent. I cannot help but believe that the body would find it difficult to digest these foreign ingredients. How can foods loaded with preservatives possibly be digested at the same rate as foods which do not contain anything unnatural?

When I conversed with patients who had been taking the Hoxsey tonic for some time and had changed their eating habits, I found that they frequently mentioned weight loss. Especially for men, 30 pounds seemed to be an average loss, and once arriving at this plateau the weight stabilized.

I remember that during the first three months of my restricted diet I felt as if my entire system was being cleansed. Since I was not into "fast foods" anyway, my weight loss was no more than 5 pounds, and I have remained at approximately the same weight since then.

I believe the stabilization of weight was largely due to the change in patients' food consumption. The foods they had been eating probably contained large amounts of preservatives, and I am convinced that the whole-some foods they began eating were more quickly and easily digested and eliminated, resulting in the weight stabilization.

Besides the addition of preservatives, there is yet another concern today that has entered the food consumption picture in this country. Bio-engineered foods have received little media coverage but should be a concern to all of us. Although testing apparently continues and only time will determine the destiny of these products, they are already in our grocery stores. Unfortunately for those who would like to know if the foods they purchase fall into this category, there is no way of knowing. The Food and Drug Administration has declared that bio-engineering in no way alters our food, going so far as to deem it unnecessary to present this information on any label.

When one considers the years the FDA sometimes spends exhaustively test-ing and retesting most products before consenting to their marketability, this almost total lack of concern regarding food is unfathomable. Considering the fact that animal testing is considered necessary for cosmet-ic and other inedible products makes the approval of bio-engineered foods—an entirely new and largely unchartered field—all the more unthinkable. In the future, if this process is found to be unsafe in any way, the damage to our health will be irreversible.

In contrast, in what appears to be in complete conflict and inconsistency with the seemingly immediate approval of bio-engineered foods, is a seem-ingly strong suspicion by the FDA of a popular cosmetic treatment, as it has not been approved. This popular, non-surgical, simple process reduces facial wrinkles without any side effects. It has been used extensively for the past six years in 61 different countries. According to a recent report on nation-al television, many women from this country have been traveling to Europe to avail themselves of the easy and effective treatment. The report included interviews with a few women, showing before and after pictures. I cannot help but wonder what measure or means is used in deciding what consti-tutes a "concern," when bio-engineering is readily approved but a harmless cosmetic procedure is not.

Europe, however, feels differently about this new process. Foods altered by bio–engineering methods are not sold in any European countries, and they refuse to buy such foods from the United States. They are taking precautions, and with good reason, I feel. The process is too new to determine the long-range health effects on consumers. European countries have even gone so far as to rip up fields containing bio–engineered crops.

With Europe taking precautions, it seems highly negligent on our part not to do a little more questioning, in an area where serious concerns should clearly be raised. Also, the fact that a large quantity of bio-engineered vegetables has already been consumed by unwary buyers is inconsistent with the principal of free choice. This is certainly an area where I feel Americans should insist on labeling, yet there appears to be little concern. This is quite possibly a case of not knowing the issues, or of not realizing the potential effects of eating altered foods because media coverage has been almost non-existent.

Fortunately, at least one informative book has been written on this subject. The author, Kathleen Hart, worked for a company which was interested in this new field, so she went to Europe to cover protests regarding bio-engineered foods there. Amazed at how little coverage there was on the subject in the States, she began her own research. Her book, entitled Eating in the Dark, includes a review of a study in which pollen from genetically engineered plants killed Monarch butterflies. This study found it's way briefly into the news in this country, but it apparently raised little concern for Americans.

The monarch butterflies dying in the fields after being exposed to the bio-engineered crops brings to mind a very old method miners had of making certain the air in a mine was safe. A small bird was brought into the mine at the beginning of the workday, remaining with them until their shift was over. I once even heard that each miner had his own bird, somehow enclosed in a small cage in the miner's hat. Whether the hat part is true or not, the fact is that the birds were there in the mine, and were far more susceptible to noxious gasses than the miners were. If his bird died, the miner knew he should leave the mine. Hopefully, the death of the Monarchs, apparently due to their sensitivity to the bio-engineered plants in the fields, is not a parallel to the seemingly non–existent yet toxic fumes in the mine. The book is truly food for thought.

Chapter 5

Alternative Approaches...?

Several years ago, not long after I started on the Hoxsey treatment, it was announced that there would be a special report on TV regarding alternative places for treating cancer. If this announcement had been made a few years later, I would not have been as surprised and shocked as I was by what I saw when I watched it. But at the time, since everything was new to me, I was certain that the Bio-Medical Center would be one of the places discussed, and I was very anxious to hear what would be said.

As it turned out, the Bio-Medical Center was not part of this program. It became evident, almost from the outset that the producers had gone out of their way to find the most bizarre places, and the most outrageous treatments possible. All of the alternative places were located across the border in Mexico—and to give just one example of the treatments reviewed—a woman was shown being placed in a small cave, where she was to spend an undetermined amount of time alone.

Nothing I saw and heard made any sense to me. The program totally disregarded the positive aspect of an alternative approach to getting well. Without a doubt, it was presented to dissuade anyone who might have considered such a path. But to me, the truly sad part of the program was the obvious "fun" the producers must have had as they ridiculed the poor, gullible, sick people whom they filmed as these patients hoped somehow, in spite of the outrageous approaches shown, that a miracle cure would come about for them.

I could not believe what I had just seen—that anyone with an ounce of human decency could make such a mockery of others, and advertise a program as "informative" which was anything but. It's no wonder that most people, upon hearing I had chosen an alternative cancer treatment, could scarcely believe I was doing so. Biased information such as that presented by the TV program was no doubt all they had ever seen or heard.

Shortly after watching the program, I asked Marta to check alternative treatments on the Web, wondering if these same biased ideas would be found there. I also wondered if she could find any information regarding the Bio-Medical Center or the Hoxsey treatment. Marta found a few articles regarding Hoxsey. The first, entitled "Hoxsey—How Healing Becomes a Crime," states that the Clinic was exiled to Mexico, where it still claims an 80% success rate. The second, entitled "History of Hoxsey Treatment," briefly outlines the Clinic's history, noting that the treatments were especially effective with skin cancer (including melanoma) and breast cancer.

The third item she found, "Alternative Medicine: An Outline for Physicians," was quite different. Among the many alternative and "unconventional" systems of diagnosis and treatment, Hoxsey is listed. There is an introduction to all of the various alternative places (geared toward any number of various diseases), in which the systems and treatments are repeatedly condemned as quackery. Doctors are warned that they are certain to encounter several of these systems as soon as they start seeing patients. It implies that everything outside of the conventional is humorous, going so far as to say it is hoped the doctor will have as much fun as they did (apparently meaning in putting together the information for the Web) when doctors encounter patients seeking such treatment. Here, Hoxsey is referred to as a "remedy" of "pink medicine" along with a "weird cleansing diet." The only explanation for such a report, discrediting all alternatives, would be to benefit those associated with traditional treatments.

I have not seen any recent televised programs on alternative cancer treatments, but information on the Web was recently called to my attention, so I looked into it, quite sure things had surely improved. I decided to contact a center on the Web that specifically noted it dealt with Mexican clinics that were using alternative cancer treatments. Although this center was located in the States instead of Mexico (which seemed unusual), I decided to get in touch with them. According to the information listed on their website, this center had been dedicated to researching and providing information for several years, and requested feedback if you were to go to any of the clinics for treatment. They were anxious to hear of any experience, positive or negative.

Along with several other places, the Bio-Medical Center is listed on this site. I noticed there were a few testimonials posted regarding clinics and treatments, but none that were familiar to me, and none indicating the many years of wellness I had come to know. Since they did not have a testimonial for the Bio-Medical Center or the Hoxsey treatment, I called the office phone number included on the site, explained I had been at the Bio-Medical Center and said that I would like to include a testimonial for this place, as I was quite familiar with it and there was nothing included on their website about it. I was told to e-mail the testimonial to them so they could include it, which I did. After waiting for a considerable length of time, my testimonial failed to appear, so I contacted the office again. I was told that some of their employees had been on vacation and they were a little behind. They also suggested I send my testimonial again, as they were not certain they could locate the original one I'd sent. After sending it again, and again finding it failed to materialize on the Web, I called again. This time I was told a picture would be necessary. In spite of the fact that none of the other published testimonials included a picture, I sent one off, feeling that if it meant a positive testimonial of the Bio-Medical Center would appear, it was worth it.

After many weeks it was obvious that my testimonial would not be appearing on this site, so I contacted another "Alternative Cancer Treatment" website. As before, this center was also located in this country, but in a different state. I called and spoke to a woman, stating that I would like to offer information regarding an alternative treatment I had used. Somehow, it was difficult to get this point across, as she seemed convinced that I was calling to make a donation.

In my attempt to make her understand, I finally read part of what was stated on the Web "if you wanted to contribute information," and I noted that details of the therapies were requested, as they were looking for more data. Apparently she did not take information, only donations, and turned me over to a man named Adolph, who would advise me as to the procedure to follow to have a testimonial appear.

In spite of the fact that all kinds of information had been requested, Adolph made it clear that he could not depend on testimonials, and that scientific proof was required. Now, according to Webster, a testimonial is "a writing or certificate in favor of…the value of a thing…a token of regard or admiration…or the like." As I tried to explain that my signature would be included on whatever I would send—this should be all that would be required for a testimonial.

Adolph stated that he would need a statement signed by a doctor, giving all facts about my cancer, along with a signed document that would prove scientifically that my cure was brought about by the alternative treatment I had used. He stated that unless my treatment could be substantiated in this manner, he refused to incorporate it onto the website. He then stated that for all he knew, I had never had cancer—and he wondered how I could be sure if I had ever really had it. He was, of course, suggesting that wherever I went, the wool could have been pulled over my eyes. Needless to say, it was quite evident to me, after this conversation, that any information I could possibly amass would never be sufficient as far as Adolph was concerned.

It occurred to me that a great many people would be more than happy to have testimonials about their experiences and alternative procedures included in various websites, but are prevented from doing so by the bureaucratic red–tape, and people like Adolph who unfortunately are able to pull strings—denying people from voicing their experiences—when they should be open–minded and receptive.

With or without information on the Web, people will continue to seek out the Bio-Medical Center. Their reputation will continue to be spread by word–of–mouth as it has for many, many years. Surely there could be no better way to hear of a place than that.

Chapter 6

Harry Hoxsey's Legacy

Harry Hoxsey has been associated with curing cancer for many, many years. In 1924 he opened his first Clinic in Illinois, and by the 1950's there were 17 additional clinics, with the primary Hoxsey Cancer Clinic located in Dallas. Hoxsey's reputation had spread nationwide.

For 35 years, in spite of the fact that the Hoxsey tonic had cured thousands of people of cancer, Harry Hoxsey spent a great deal of time in court in order to keep his clinics open. The AMA labeled him a fake and a quack and engaged in every conceivable means to put him out of business. The slanderous and offensive treatment he suffered was unbelievable. Yet he insisted on continuing to help people. To say he was a dedicated and self-less man simply does not do him justice. The legacy of healing that continues today would not be available without his determination, fortitude and dedication to healing.

What was really going on? Why was Harry Hoxsey pursued so relentlessly? The picture is indeed very clear. If the AMA, even for a moment, believed that Harry Hoxsey was truly a fake it would not have been necessary for them to take any action. If he was not curing cancer patients, who would be more aware of this than the patients themselves? If this had been the case, the clinics would have simply ceased to exist, without any outside influence. However, the threat to recognized medicine was very real. Hundreds of people were being cured. Yes—I believe Harry Hoxsey's 17 successful clinics were a very real threat.

Cancer is a very old disease. It was known in Egypt 4500 years ago and in India 4000 years ago. Surgery, a method that began almost 2000 years ago, is the most ancient of all cancer treatments. Indeed, organized medicine today still considers surgery one of the most reliable weapons.

Obviously, cancer was also known in this country in the 1800's when, as a result of an unexplained cure experienced by one of farmer John Hoxsey's horses, he began experimenting with plants and flowers to see if he could come up with a cure. The horse had been put out to pasture when John Hoxsey could not bear to destroy the horse after it was diagnosed with cancer. Grazing on a variety of plants in the pasture the animal was cured. (Perhaps this could relate to animals' instinct to heal themselves). At any rate, John Hoxsey set up his lab and began experimenting—grinding flowers and leaves, mashing berries, boiling roots, trying formula after formula. Eventually, by 1840, he came up with three separate formulas that proved to be very effective on animals. One was oral, one a powder and the third a salve. The news of Mr. Hoxsey's successful formulas traveled quickly, and farmers came from far away with their animals, having heard they could be cured. The Hoxsey formulas were passed down from father to son and were eventually passed to Harry Hoxsey's father, who was the first person to try them on humans. Found to be equally successful on people, many traveled great distances to seek treatment, resulting in hundreds of people being cured.

In 1915, when Harry Hoxsey was just 15 years old, his father became ill and was unable to work. Harry had to quit school, working in coal mines and as a mule driver to help support the family. He had grown up watching his father cure cancer patients, which instilled in Harry the desire to become a doctor. Harry's goal was to cure patients as his father had, but with a license—he knew it was a crime to practice medicine without one. He realized that no matter how many patients he might save, if one died while in his care (even if every doctor in the country had previously given him up as hopeless) he could be arrested and convicted of manslaughter if he was unlicensed. Shortly before the elder Mr. Hoxsey died, he passed the formula on to Harry, because of all of his children Harry was the most determined to become a doctor.

In his book, Harry relates the following, spoken by his father when he gave Harry the formulas:

> "Now you have the power to heal the sick and save lives...I've cured a few hundred people; you can cure thousands...." Then his father went on to say: "But it's not only a gift, son; it's a trust and a great responsibility. Abe Lincoln once said that God must love the common people, because He made so many of them. We're common, ordinary people. No matter how high you go, you must never lose touch with the common people. You must never refuse to treat anybody because he cannot pay. Promise me that."

This is the promise Harry Hoxsey made. He was 17 years old. At the same time, Harry's father stated that he wished he could help him by sending him to college and medical school. He realized Harry would have a long, hard battle ahead. Little did his father realize what a difficult battle it would be, and how right his prediction would prove.

Since it was well known for miles around the small town in Illinois where they lived that Harry's father could cure cancer, people continued arriving at the door asking Harry to cure them. At first he refused, but then he did start curing people, realizing that if he didn't, some people would be dead before he could become a doctor.

News of Harry's treatments and cured patients spread to the medical community. Doctors and investigators arrived. Recovered patients were interviewed—not only Harry's patients but his fathers patients as well. Dr. Bruce Miller, one of the investigating doctors, accompanied Harry while he was treating a grievously ill patient. The doctor felt the patient was so ill that she would certainly not survive. Harry said she had already improved, and he was confident she would recover—which she did. After this incident, Dr. Miller listened as Harry told the doctor of his plan to attend medical school and become a doctor. Harry recorded the following statement, made by Dr. Miller:

"One of the things we doctors know little about is cancer...we don't know how to stop their wild propagation, nor how to prevent them [cancers] from spreading...any sincere doctor will admit that surgery and x-ray are useless once the disease has metastasized...we're groping for a more effective treatment." Dr. Miller then continued: "The point I'm making is this: We can't permit an uninitiated layman like you to come up with a solution to a medical problem that has baffled the best scientific minds for thousands of years. If we did, public confidence in the omniscience of the priesthood would be undermined...our incomes would be threatened." Then Dr. Miller asserted what to Harry Hoxsey was a death sentence to his future: "You don't stand a chance, you'll never get in. I've made inquiries, talked to doctors...they're out to get you...they've already complained to the State Board...practicing without a license...promoting a 'fake' cure...you're blackballed, no medical school will let you in the door."

However, Dr. Miller apparently realized that the tonic did cure cancer, for he joined Harry in setting up the Clinic in Taylorsville, Illinois, and was with him for several years.

After the investigation, attempts were made by the AMA to purchase the formulas, but they refused to consider treating everyone the way Harry had promised his father. It was more than clear that profit was their main interest. When Harry refused to cooperate, he realized what he would now be up against. He was not only refused admission to a medical school but was called a quack and a fake. The attacks were continuous and on January 2, 1926, the official Journal of the AMA resorted to attacking his father's memory with numerous distortions as well, stating that his powders ate into blood vessels, that patients bled to death, and several other slanderous untruths.

An influential figure at this time was Dr. William Halsted. He pioneered medical procedures in the late 1800's, continued his work into the early 1900's, and is still highly regarded in the medical world today. He advocated the use of surgical gloves, and in the late 1800's (due to influences from his formal training in Germany) founded the surgical training program at Johns Hopkins University, which became a model for many others.

In his experimental work with various potential anesthesia, Dr. Halsted became addicted to cocaine, and later to morphine and alcohol. In 1886, and again in 1887, he was admitted to Butler Hospital for treatment, and although he was discharged he continued to abuse morphine until the time of his death in 1922.

Dr. Halsted's greatest contribution appears to be as a surgical educator. He is best known for the "radical" mastectomy, where not only the breast is removed, but all of the tissue right down to the bones of the chest, as well. This was one of the options explained to me after my surgery as the possible next step eight years ago.

This radical surgery was the accepted form of treatment recommended by the AMA for breast cancer when Harry Hoxsey opened his first Clinic in the early 1920's, and this radical approach remained in effect as the standard treatment for breast cancers of all types and sizes until the 1970's, at which time lumpectomies and other less radical procedures were introduced.

Ironically, as late as October of 2002, the results of two independent studies appeared in the local newspaper to which I subscribe. The first, a European study on just over 700 cancer patients, compares the survival rates between those who had radical mastectomies and patients who had lumpectomies or partial mastectomies and radiation. This study found that the survival rates for either are almost identical. The other, a U.S. government funded study of 1,800 cancer patients, compares the same medical procedures and comes up with almost the same results as the European study. According to this study, radical mastectomy patients had a survival rate of 58.8%, while those treated by lumpectomy and radiation showed a 58.3% survival rate.

Due to the results of these studies, it was declared that the shift was away from radical mastectomy, a procedure which had "long dominated" the field of breast cancer treatment. The studies confirm that the "radical" procedure, introduced so many years ago, is far from totally outmoded, in spite of the fact that less invasive procedures have entered the picture. Unfortunately, the results of these (independent) studies also show a lower survival rate for either treatment option than what I had previously been led to believe.

However, Harry Hoxsey was not the only person during the 1920's who questioned the accepted forms of cancer treatment in favor of internal treatments. There were well–known doctors at the time who were also developing some different views of cancer treatment. Dr. Robert Bell, who was head of the Cancer Research Department of Battersea Hospital in England, as well as vice–president of the International Society for Cancer Research, recorded the following in the New York Medical Record, March 18, 1922:

> "Cancer is rooted in every drop of blood in the body and we may as well expect to stop the growing of apples by picking them off trees, or to stop the springing of dandelions by cutting off the blossoms and leaving the root in the ground, as to expect to destroy malignancy in the human body by attacking the outward growth."

Despite Dr. Bell's exalted positions, his unorthodox view that cancer is a blood disease, and his written attacks upon "surgery and irradiation" as an effective treatment of cancer led officials of the British Medical Society to publicly label him a "quack." He sued for libel and slander and won a court decision with damages amounting to approximately $50,000.

Numerous other medical authorities at this time agreed that the treatment of cancer by "surgery and/or irradiation" is usually followed by another recurrence of the disease. (According to Webster's dictionary, "irradiation" means "...to treat by radiant heat...to treat by exposure to radiation"). These assertions were repeated in later years by other doctors. For example, to name a few: Dr. L. Duncan Bulkley, senior surgeon at New York Skin and Cancer Hospital stated, "Cancer is not a surgical disease. Neither surgery, x-ray nor radium has changed in any way whatever the ultimate mortality of cancer in 40 years." A similar statement was made by Dr. W.A. Dewey who had been a professor of medicine at the University of Michigan. And as late as 1955 famous Mayo Clinic surgeon Dr. O. Theron Clagett, addressed the Society of Graduate Surgeons of Los Angeles County, declaring that surgery, with a few exceptions was not the answer to cancer, and stated that he was certain cancer would eventually be cured by drugs. In spite of numerous doctors thinking otherwise, on December 21, 1946, The Saturday Evening Post stated: "A doctor who claims to know an effective treatment for cancer not involving surgery, radium or x-ray is an ipso facto quack."

In 1898 George Henry Simmons became editor of the AMA Journal. At that time it was a little known publication, but "Doc" Simmons as he became known had ambitious plans. His idea was to turn the AMA into a giant trust, dominating the entire healing profession. By the end of 1903 the organization had tripled in size with a total membership of 30,000. In effect, Doc Simmons was the AMA, referring to himself as "Spokesman for American Medicine."

He began a crusade against "quacks and charlatans" in the healing profession. Eventually it also included the so–called "irregulars" which included Christian Science practitioners, osteopaths, chiropractors and homeopathic physicians. Slanderous and distorted stories were planted in newspapers and magazines. The AMA proclaimed that their intent was to protect the public against "medical bandits." At the same time, the AMA began to set standards for medical education and training.

In his later years, Doc Simmons became involved in a personal scandal and was forced to resign. His protégée Morris Fishbein then took over the reins of the AMA. Morris Fishbein not only took over where Doc Simmons left off but accelerated the effort and became even more venomous to anyone in the healing profession outside of the AMA. Identifying himself as Editor for the AMA, he wrote daily columns for popular magazines and newspapers giving medical advice, which were syndicated all over the country. The California Medical Society protested, saying Fishbein's column was full of "medical inaccuracies and misstatements."

During those years, Harry Hoxsey was charged with practicing without a license, although he explained that he himself was not treating patients. The patients were actually being treated by doctors in the clinics, and since the clinics were well-staffed, there were obviously quite a few doctors who realized the Hoxsey formulas were curing patients. Also, it should have been clear that Harry alone could not be treating patients in 17 different areas at once.

Constantly during the years Harry Hoxsey urged investigation be made of his clinics, even sending the invitation to Morris Fishbein personally to get a "first hand look at our method of treating cancer." The only response was further untrue remarks in the Journal. To this Harry Hoxsey remarks in his book "I'd rather be notorious and save people's lives, than famous and bury them."

Not only was Harry himself slandered, but also emergency rooms refused to treat patients who were known to have been patients at a Hoxsey Clinic. The AMA relentlessly hounded Harry Hoxsey, bringing him to court on "quackery" charges. Once, during a two-month period, he was served with seven warrants for his arrest. When he was charged with operating without a license, he finally found it easier to just plead guilty and pay the $100 fine, so he could return to his patients.

Sometimes, when he appeared in court on various charges, as many as 100 to 150 patients accompanied him, all willing to testify in his defense. And the courts, it seemed, could not find a law against saving lives.

The most spectacular case during Harry Hoxsey's long career curing cancer took place in Galesburg, Illinois. On March 2, 1930 Harry saw a patient named Mandus Johnson. The entire top of his head was covered with a cancer, with the diagnostic biopsy made by a Dr. Baird of Galesburg. The cancer consumed the entire scalp, the skull was exposed, and two drain tubes had been inserted into holes cut into the skull from which pus drained every day. Treatment began; an application of powder was applied. The yellow powder causes the cancer to blacken, and in a few weeks a hard crust forms (depending on the size of the cancer, this takes approximately 4 weeks) and the cancer starts shrinking and pulling away. And while the powder has this dramatic effect on cancer, it has no effect whatsoever on normal skin. After this it separates completely from the normal tissue and can be lifted out. In Mr. Johnson's case, on April 8th, 5 weeks after his treatment had begun, the top of his skull was removed and the cancer was removed with it.

This case received a great deal of publicity and the AMA Journal published a vicious article asserting Johnson had died as a result of the treatment. This lie, however, was brought to light on Decoration Day, May 30th, 1930, when the "dead man" made a personal appearance with over 100 other Hoxsey patients at a giant demonstration in Weed Park, Muscatine, Iowa. The crowd in the park that day was said to number 32,000. Mendus Johnson lived for 30 years after this amazing cure. In Harry Hoxsey's book, You Don't Have to Die, there are pictures of Mr. Johnson, showing the cancer before treatment and also the top of his head after it had been healed.

By the end of the 1950's, the AMA—even while finally admitting the tonic does "cure" some cases of cancer—branded Harry Hoxsey the "worst quack of the century." They continually sought to put him out of business by constantly taking him to court. There was no doubt, however, that Hoxsey was curing cancer, because so many recovered patients continued to testify on his behalf. Finally, he won a slander suit against Dr. Morris Fishbein, who was the current head of the Journal of the AMA, a position of ultimate power and influence. In newspaper interviews before this trial, Morris Fishbein boasted, "I have never lost a case or settled out of court." Despite these assertions, Fishbein's attorney, Richard Scurry, apparently felt Harry had a good case, for he strongly urged an out-of-court settlement. Harry refused. He was determined to prove in open court that the charges that had been broadcast for more than 25 years were vicious lies. In this 1950's trial, the court upheld the fact that Harry Hoxsey cured people of cancer and that the utterances of Morris Fishbein were false, slanderous and libelous. The jury of 12 men found that the Hoxsey treatment cures cancer. Not only had Harry Hoxsey won this suit against Dr. Fishbein, but Fishbein was completely discredited.

Hoxsey retained great popular appeal despite unrelenting opposition by the medical profession. All manner of tactics were used to try to ruin his reputation, including the posting of notices in Post Offices warning people to stay away from the clinics. In the video The Quack Who Cured Cancer, Mildred Nelson talks about these notices, with many patients reporting to her that they had removed and destroyed them. These repeated occurrences clearly demonstrated how many people felt.

Amidst the false accusations against him, Harry Hoxsey continued to invite members of the AMA and the FDA or the Federal Government to come and check the thousands of case histories in his files but no one ever came. It was clear that to do so would give credibility to the Hoxsey treatments, so an investigation never took place. The overwhelming popularity and success of the Hoxsey clinics (in 1956 his Dallas clinic alone had approximately 10,000 cases under constant treatment or observation) had little effect against the power and influence of the AMA. In the end, the combined pressures of organized medicine and the FDA closed Harry Hoxsey down.

The Hoxsey clinics were not the only alternative medical establishments that felt the pressure of the AMA. Laws discriminating against "irregular" medical groups were enacted, greatly restricting some groups, including chiropractors and placing strict limitations on others. Memories of these insidious and malicious untruths still linger today, affecting some branches of medicine. Finally, through the combined efforts of the AMA and the FDA, all of the clinics were closed. Officials descended and in a single day shut down every Clinic. Harry's heart had begun to fail, and he did not have enough money to initiate a fight to re-open his clinics. In 1963 he encouraged his chief nurse Mildred Nelson to move the Clinic across the border into Mexico. Mr. Herbert Spencer makes the following appropriate statement in the introduction to Harry Hoxsey's book, You Don't Have to Die:

"There is a principle which is a bar against all information, which is proof against all argument, and which cannot fail to keep a man in everlasting ignorance. That principle is condemnation without investigation."

Having been with the Clinic for many years, Mildred Nelson was an obvious choice to take over its management. Mildred's mother had been diagnosed with cancer years before and insisted on going to the Hoxsey Clinic in Dallas, much against her daughter's wishes and recommendations.

Mildred was a member of the medical community, having been trained in the traditional medical treatments for cancer. Her mother insisted, however, and Mildred, who planned to stay and observe for a couple of weeks in order to change her mother's mind, saw patients getting better. She never left. Her mother was cured of cancer and outlived all of her doctors. And Mildred Nelson remained at the clinic for the rest of her life.

Harry encouraged Mildred to drop the name "Hoxsey" in relation to the new Clinic in Tijuana, as there had been so much negative publicity. However, although Mildred did name the Clinic in Mexico the Bio-Medical Center, she insisted that the treatment retain the name Hoxsey.

It is interesting to me that the media frequently warns us to avoid certain foods which reportedly contribute to cancer. The fats in potato chips and fried foods have been mentioned, and from time to time a certain food receives great attention, only to have these statements either retracted, or at least (at a later date) found to be not quite as bad as originally thought. The fact remains, however, that whatever the food might be, it is nevertheless eaten. Maybe I'm missing something here, but my unscientific mind leads me to believe that it would be impossible for these consumed foods to stay out of the bloodstream. However, since cancers are routinely treated by surgical removal or radiation applied to a certain area, it seems this is what many medical people would like us to believe. Do we need scientific tests to make sure all that we eat affects our blood? Somehow it just seems all too logical that the entire system should be considered when cancer occurs.

From the beginning, Harry Hoxsey considered cancer a systemic disease, however localized it might appear. Hence, his therapy emphasizes and aims to restore normalcy to the entire body. While skin cancers and some other malignancies might be treated with the powder or the salve, the tonic is always part of the treatment. At the Bio-Medical Center the entire system is always considered, the goal being it's return to normalcy.

In light of my own case and countless others like mine, it is not surprising that the Bio-Medical Center treats 100 or more patients each week from all over the world. Thousands have stepped through the doors of the Clinic and reclaimed their lives as a result.

Note: Selections and quotes in this chapter from You Don't Have to Die *by Harry Hoxsey (1956) included with permission.*

Part 4

Conclusion

An Interesting and Thoughtful Journey

When I was first diagnosed, and began taking notes in the doctor's office, recording various recommendations, little did I realize that these notes would result in the writing of this book. If anyone had suggested such a thing at that time, I would have said the idea was crazy.

In fact, looking back, even taking notes at the onset was completely out of character for me. I had never kept a diary or journal of any kind, and taking notes simply to remember a conversation was something I had never done before. Even less characteristic was that I held onto these notes and continued to record events and conversations, resulting in a very large envelope into which I had deposited dozens and dozens of pieces of paper. This accumulated jigsaw puzzle of notes reflected the events of the previous eight years.

Long ago, when Bonny told me of Eva finding a cure for her cancer south of the border, it never occurred to me that "that herbal place" she spoke of was located in Mexico because it had been driven out of our country. I did not even question, at the time, why there was not such a place in the States. Why did I not wonder why one would have to cross the border to find an herbal cure, if this would be the path one chose to take? Why should such a treatment not be available in the States?

The past few years have been quite a journey. Looking back, I realize my experiences only underscore the adage that "truth is stranger than fiction." If I had not lived them myself, I would have found them hard to believe. Somehow, from the onset, I found strengths I never realized I had, and found I could not be swayed by other people's opinions no matter how forcibly their ideas were presented.

These experiences and events only seem to emphasize the fact that everything happens for a reason. So often during these years, information seemed to simply fall into my lap. Sometimes it would happen in the most unexpected ways, such as the time Anjie handed me the copy of the animal rights magazine with the article about the unfortunate mares and colts. It was not Anjie's habit to share magazine articles about animals with me, as not only is she bombarded with information regarding animal abuse, but she is also frequently out of the office. I realized immediately, of course, how significant the article was to my book. However, it was not until months later that I found out how truly remarkable it was that I had received it. Anjie had never subscribed to this publication, but had simply received a couple of complimentary copies. The copy she handed me that day was the last she received.

Sometimes, a seemingly inconsequential sentence would trigger a new thought. This could happen during a conversation, while listening to the radio, reading a publication, or in any number of other ways. Often these sentences or thoughts would come to me at night. More often than not, while the message was always brief, there was never a doubt in my mind as to what it was referring. As my book progressed, I became more aware of "the voice within," and more aware of intuitive feelings, knowing I should listen. I know without a doubt that God has been my guiding spirit.

My friend Tom, who works as a paramedic, is very in tune with his inner voice, and has come to know how beneficial these instincts can be. He told me of an experience he had once while taking a seriously ill patient to the hospital. He was driving the ambulance that day and he knew the quickest way to the hospital would be to take the expressway. However, as he started out, he had the strongest feeling that he should take another route, which was slightly longer and somewhat slower even when he turned on his lights and siren. Following his instincts, he stayed off the highway. As he neared the hospital, at a place where he could clearly see the expressway, he noticed that there had apparently been a major accident because the traffic was at a total standstill. His patient survived, but had he not followed the dictates of his "inner voice" that day, things might have turned out quite differently.

It is not always easy to listen to or pay attention to our intuitive feelings or instincts, even though we've all experienced them from time to time. We have all been taught certain expected behaviors and guidelines in school, at home, and at work, and to deviate from them seems irresponsible. These "learned" responses govern our thinking. Sometimes, what is considered "common sense" also overrides or blocks out our intuitive feelings. To some extent this "common sense" concept, as important as it is in many situations, also prevents many people from being completely open-minded and receptive to new ideas.

The ability to be open-minded, especially medically speaking, is much easier said than done. This fact became very evident to me a couple of years ago, shortly after I heard the news of Eva's death. I knew she had been having heart problems and to the best of my knowledge she died of heart failure. Ironically, not long after hearing the news, I had an unexpected conversation with Violet, a friend of Eva's. I had met Violet only once before, and then only briefly, but she had known Eva well and spoke of Eva's trip to the Bio-Medical Center years before. Violet spoke of Eva's heart problems, and said that Eva had told her attending physician how she had, approximately 25 years before, taken the Hoxsey tonic and been cured of cancer. She related to the doctor that three physicians at the time had all confirmed her cancer diagnosis, giving her six months to live unless she went through with the recommended amputation. Throughout the time he treated her, her doctor adamantly refused to believe that she had been cured of cancer, saying she must never have had it in the first place.

Violet was incensed. She could not believe that the doctor would simply discount all that Eva told him. How could this doctor prefer to believe that three doctors could all make the same horrifically incorrect diagnosis and recommend amputation, instead of accepting the fact that Eva had been cured by a process he was unfamiliar with? His total disregard for what Eva said prompted Violet to say, "He should have known she was having trouble with her heart, not her head." I am certain that Eva's doctor, like so many doctors today, had not dealt with many cancer patients who live for 25 years after treatment. For this reason, Eva's claim seemed impossible to him—so much so that he discounted it completely. (According to a recent statistical report compiled by the American Cancer Society, the 5-year relative survival rates for cancer had tripled to 62% (3 in 5). What would the chances for those surviving five years be to live twenty years longer?).

It is frustrating to hear about a mind so closed to the possibility of a cure brought about by a process or treatment that is not in accord with conventional means. It would seem, as highly educated medical professionals, that they should be inquisitive about it rather than simply disregard it. After all, by whatever means, if a person gets well, it is a cure nonetheless.

America has made great strides over the past few years, surgically speaking. Most people are aware of at least some of the new and finer techniques in the field of surgery. I cannot help but feel that medically speaking the emphasis has been in this area, while other areas have obvious shortcomings. Despite the great strides made in infant surgery, and although some premature and very small infants have been saved by these new surgical procedures, our infant death rate is a stark reminder that surgery alone is not enough. (The last time I saw a statistical worldwide report, the United States was tenth in the world — nine countries had a lower infant death rate than we). Whatever we might chalk this up to, it cannot in anyway be an acceptable answer or excuse.

It seems that pride and exaggerated self confidence has kept the medical profession slow to accept procedures used in other countries. Acupuncture, which has been used successfully for over a thousand years but has just recently been accepted here, is a good example of this. And Germany, through Dr. Hans Neiper's research and theories established years ago, has greatly helped many multiple sclerosis patients. One of my very good friends traveled to Germany approximately 25 years ago, and has fared far better than most people treated for MS here. Dr. Napier placed great emphasis on diet, vitamins, and food supplements—simple solutions that could help many but are apparently very slow to be accepted by doctors in the States. Perhaps like the Hoxsey tonic, it just seems too simple to truly work.

Judging from experiences I've had, and after listening to the opinions of many people, I've concluded that the medical profession has largely accomplished it's mission of promoting itself (and it's treatments) as the only viable option. Somehow, something new and different—even if it shows promise—is not to be trusted and is to be avoided at all costs.

This phenomenon reminds me of the right to use sweat lodges, which were taken away from all Native Americans in the late 1800's. Laws were enacted, and anyone caught participating in a sweat ceremony could be arrested. To make the use of sweat lodges illegal for all Native Americans effectively cut off their rights to spirituality, having the same effect as permanently closing the doors to someone's church or temple. It not only eliminated a sacred part of Indian life, but, as far as the white community was concerned, did away with a ceremony that (since it was generally not understood) held an element of fear for those unfamiliar with it. Not until the time of President Carter's term in office was the right to participate in this ancient, sacred ceremony returned to the Indians. Perhaps we need another spokesperson, with the same kind of authority held by the President, to return to this country the right to have convenient access to a place like the Bio-Medical Center.

Just as grass manages to grow—even breaking through cracks along broad modern highways— relentless in it's determination to survive, so should our determination be in acknowledging alternative possibilities in spite of the obstacles. I believe the time has come when we must be willing to stand back and take a critical, open-minded view of all things. No discoveries can be made unless we are willing to try something new, and no discoveries can be made unless we are willing to not be right. As George Sand was reportedly heard to say:

"Let us accept truth, even when it surprises us and alters our views."

I like to think that the day will come when all approaches to medicine will be considered, with the patient's well being the top priority. There will be no competition, the best procedures will be utilized, and everything will be kept in perspective, welcoming procedures and treatments from every corner of the world. When it will not matter, and no one will care which procedure, medicine, treatment, or doctor caused a cure. Then we will all be winners—everyone will reach the finish line together.

Several months ago, I tried to contact Neale Donald Walsh to request permission to quote a passage from his book Conversations with God. Unfortunately, my attempts to contact him have proven unsuccessful. Therefore, I have taken it upon myself to use his wonderful passage. This quote expresses my thoughts and feelings much better than I could ever hope to, and says all I aspire to convey in closing:

"There is no master race. There is no greatest nation. There is no one true religion. There is no inherently perfect philosophy. There is no always right political party, morally supreme economic system, or one and only way to Heaven.

"Erase these ideas from your memory. Eliminate them from your experience. Eradicate them from your culture. For these are thoughts of division and separation, and people have killed each other over these thoughts. Only this thought (truth) will save you: We are all one."

Endnotes

Hoxsey's Bio-Medical Center (The Experience) Video. Available from Carol Main at www.afinerview.com.

Michael Gearin-Tosh, Living Proof: A Medical Mutiny (Scribner, New York, 2002).

Hoxsey–The Quack Who Cured Cancer Video. (The Bio-Medical Center, Tijuana, Mexico).

Eating in the Dark – America's Experiment with Genetically Engineered Food
by Kathleen Hart
Patheon Books

With special thanks to Johannah, who not only edited this book, but with great patience constantly set about to include the thoughts and additions as my inner voice beckoned or new information appeared. The work is not mine alone.

Further Information

Suggested Reading:

You Don't Have to Die
by Harry M. Hoxsey, ND
Copyright 1956
Book available from the Bio-Medical Center
(Selections from this book included in Part 3, Chapter 6 are printed with permission.)

When Healing Becomes a Crime – The Story of the Hoxsey Cancer Clinics
by Kenny Ausubel
Book available from the Bio-Medical Center

Living Proof – A Medical Mutiny
by Michael Gearin-Tosh
Scribner, New York

Eating in the Dark – America's Experiment with Genetically Engineered Food
by Kathleen Hart
Patheon Books

Videos
Hoxsey – The Quack Who Cured Cancer
Hoxsey's Bio-Medical Center
Hoxsey's Bio-Medical Center – The Experience
(All videos are available from the Bio-Medical Center)

World Wide Web Information
History of Hoxsey Treatment, by Patricia Spain Ward, PhD
William Halsted (1852-1992), by S.J. Parker;
www.surgical-tutor.org.UK

Web MD with AOL Health; Re: Information on breast cancer
Morris Fishbein–AMA Enemy of Amercian Health by Bob Wallace Law;
www.rockwell.com

Bio-Medical Center

Street Address:
3170 General Ferreira, Col. Madero Sur.
Tijuana, Baja Calafornia
22150 Mexico

Mailing Address:
P.O. Box 433654
San Ysidro, CA 92143

Telephone: (01152664) 684-9011
Fax: (01152664) 684-9744
email: biomedicalcenter@hotmail.com

Marie Halbrendt Carlson
P.O. Box 23
Jefferson, MA01522-0023

ISBN: 0-9723939-0-0